S Bates

SOLVING MATHS PROBLEMS

for ages 5-7

Contents

Level 1

Level 2

Introduction

It is widely recognised that there is a need for activities that address 'using and applying mathematics' through solving problems. However 'using and applying' should be exactly that. Children can only use and apply what they already know and this should include a strong grasp of number as well as knowledge of appropriate techniques and mathematical vocabulary.

In *Solving Maths Problems* we encourage the development of number skills and calculation techniques and the application of these skills to problem-solving situations. All aspects of 'using and applying mathematics' are covered through the wide range of activities in this series.

It is important to consider what we mean by the term 'problem' in mathematics. A problem can consist of a question presented in words, requiring children to 'decode' the question then to decide which mathematical processes to apply. It can also mean any mathematical activity that requires children to investigate, following logical processes. Some problems are, of course, 'closed' – a question is presented to the children and there is only one answer to the question, but the child has to make decisions over which mathematical skills to use and how to follow these through. Other problems are 'open-ended', giving children the opportunity to investigate further. This series provides a variety of both 'closed' and 'open-ended' problems.

In this book you will find several pages featuring the same type of problem. This allows for revision of techniques already learnt but also for further attempts at problems that may have presented difficulties the first time round. It is very important that children should not feel defeated by maths when they make errors – instead they should be encouraged to learn from their mistakes and to 'have another go' at a similar problem.

How to use this book

The first 56 activity sheets in this book are targeted towards Year 1. Activity sheets 57-119 are targeted towards Year 2. However, you can use any of the activity sheets with your own class, regardless of which year group you have, dependent on ability. The children must have the necessary levels of skill in number work to be able to tackle the questions posed on each activity sheet – you will need to decide which children are ready for each activity. The aim should be for children to be engaged in enjoyable activities that provide practice of mathematical skills and knowledge.

You will find that some activities are visited more than once, but using different numbers or quantities, so that children can gain repeated practice of the problem-solving skills.

Some of the sheets can be used independently, with just a small amount of support. These sheets may include 'word problems' where the questions require the children to make decisions on how to solve the problems posed. The children will gain confidence in dealing with these types of problems once they have experienced the 'discussion problems' that are also featured.

The **teachers' notes** on each activity sheet offer a suggested objective for the activity. Most sheets offer opportunities to address a wide range of objectives and you might decide to concentrate on a completely different objective, again centred on the needs of your own class. A problem is then posed. On some sheets there are also extension problems for more able children.

All of the activity sheets can also be found on the **accompanying CD-ROM** for you to print out or display on a whiteboard for group discussion. You might also decide to print out and laminate specific activity sheets for repeated use. In this way you can quickly build a bank of resources for stimulating discussion of maths and for setting problems. Answers to the activities are also on the CD-ROM where appropriate.

Assessment

Pages 4-7 feature guidelines for assessing mathematics, based on the Assessment Guidelines provided through the National Strategies. They are presented in the form of questions. You could choose to use these pages as individual record sheets - highlighting each question in green when you feel the child has a high level of achievement, in orange when you feel that the pupil is secure, and in red if you feel that the child has a low level of achievement. Alternatively, you could tick the box beside statements that you feel the child is secure in the skills specified.

Guidelines for assessing mathematics

Level 1

Using and applying mathematics

Pupils use mathematics as an integral part of classroom activities. They represent their work with objects or pictures and discuss it. They recognise and use a simple pattern or relationship.

- Do the children use mathematics as an integral part of classroom activities, eg with support? Do the children engage with practical mathematical activities involving sorting, counting and measuring by direct comparison? (Ma1 Level 1) ❑
- Do the children represent their work with objects or pictures? Do the children discuss their work? Do the children respond to questions and ideas from peers and adults? Do the children refer to the materials they have used and talk about what they have done, patterns they have noticed, etc? (Ma1 Level 1) ❑
- Do the children draw simple conclusions from their work? Do the children describe the different ways they have sorted objects, what is the same about objects in a set, how sets differ? (Ma1 Level 1) ❑

Number

Pupils count, order, add and subtract numbers when solving problems involving up to 10 objects. They read and write the numbers involved.

- Do the children count up to 10 objects? Do they estimate and check a number? Do they read and write numbers to 10? Do they order numbers to 10? (Ma2 Level 1) ❑
- Are the children beginning to use the fraction one half? (Ma2 Level 1) ❑
- Do the children understand addition as finding the total of two or more sets of objects? Do they understand subtraction as 'taking away' objects from a set and finding how many are left? (Ma2 Level 1) ❑
- Do the children add and subtract numbers of objects to 10? Are the children beginning to know some addition facts? (Ma2 Level 1) ❑
- Do the children solve addition/subtraction problems involving up to 10 objects? ❑
- Do they solve problems involving 1p or £1 coins? (Ma2 Level 1) ❑
- Do the children record their work with objects, pictures or diagrams? Are they beginning to use the symbols + and = to record additions? (Ma2 Level 1) ❑

Shape, space and measures

When working with 2-D and 3-D shapes, pupils use everyday language to describe properties and positions. They measure and order objects using direct comparison and order events.

- Do the children use everyday language to describe properties of 2-D and 3-D shapes? Do they sort shapes and say how they have selected them? Do they use properties such as large, small, triangles, roll, stack? Are they beginning to refer to some features of shapes such as side and corner? Are they beginning to name the shapes they use in the context of an activity? (Ma3 Level 1) ❑

- Do the children use everyday language to describe positions of 2-D and 3-D shapes? Do they respond to and use positional language, eg 'behind', 'under', 'on top of', 'next to', 'in between'? Do they respond to and use directional language in talk about objects and movement, eg 'forwards', 'backwards', 'turn'? (Ma3 Level 1) ❑

- Do the children measure and order objects using direct comparison? Do they order everyday events and describe the sequence? Do they use the vocabulary of time including days of the week? Do they read the time on an analogue clock at the hour and begin to know the half hour? (Ma3 Level 1) ❑

Handling data

Pupils sort objects and classify them, demonstrating the criterion they have used.

- Do the children sort and classify objects? Do they sort using one criterion or sort into disjoint sets using two simple criteria such as thick/thin? Do they sort objects again using a different criterion? Do they sort into a given large scale Venn or Carroll diagram? Do they represent their work by using the objects they have sorted as a record or using objects/pictures to create simple block graphs? (Ma4 Level 1) ❑

- Do they demonstrate the criterion they have used? Do they respond to questions about how they have sorted objects and why each object belongs in a set? Do they talk about which set has most? Do they talk about how they have represented their work? (Ma4 Level 1) ❑

❑

Guidelines for assessing mathematics

Level 2

Using and applying mathematics

Pupils select the mathematics they use in some classroom activities. They discuss their work using some mathematical language and are beginning to represent it using symbols and simple diagrams. They explain why an answer is correct.

- Do the children select the mathematics they use in some classroom activities, eg with support? Do they find a starting point, identifying key facts/relevant information? Do they use apparatus, diagrams, role-play, etc. to represent and clarify a problem? Do they move between different representations of a problem, eg a situation described in words, a diagram, etc. Do they adopt a suggested model or systematic approach? Do they make connections and apply their knowledge to similar situations? Do they use mathematical content from levels 1 and 2 to solve problems and investigate? (Ma1 Level 2) ❑

- Do the children discuss their work using mathematical language, eg with support? Do they describe the strategies and methods they use in their work? Do they engage with others' explanations, compare, evaluate? Are they beginning to represent their work using symbols and simple diagrams, eg with support? Do they use pictures, diagrams and symbols to communicate their thinking, or demonstrate a solution or process? Are they beginning to appreciate the need to record and develop their own methods of recording? (Ma1 Level 2) ❑

- Can the children explain why an answer is correct, eg with support? Can they predict what comes next in a simple number, shape or spatial pattern or sequence and give reasons for their opinion? (Ma1 Level 2) ❑

Number

Pupils count sets of objects reliably, and use mental recall of addition and subtraction facts to 10. They begin to understand the place value of each digit in a number and use this to order numbers up to 100. They choose the appropriate operation when solving addition and subtraction problems. They use the knowledge that subtraction is the inverse of addition. They use mental calculation strategies to solve number problems involving money and measures. They recognise sequences of numbers, including odd and even numbers.

- Do the children count sets of objects reliably, eg group objects in tens, twos or fives to count them? Are they beginning to understand the place value of each digit, using this to order numbers up to 100? Do they recognise sequences of numbers, including odd and even numbers, eg continue a sequence that increases or decreases in regular steps, recognise numbers from counting in tens or twos? (Ma2 Level 2) ❑

- Are the children beginning to use halves and quarters, eg in a practical context? Can they work out halves of numbers up to 20 and are they beginning to recall these? Can they relate the concept of half of a small quantity to the concept of half of a shape, eg shade one half or one quarter of a given shape? (Ma2 Level 2) ❑

- Do the children use the knowledge that subtraction is the inverse of addition, eg are they beginning to understand subtraction as 'difference'? Can they make related number sentences involving addition and subtraction? Do they understand halving as a way of 'undoing' doubling and vice versa? (Ma2 Level 2) ❑

- Do the children use mental recall of addition facts to 10, eg use place value to derive $30 + 70 = 100$ from the known fact $3 + 7 = 10$? Do they use mental calculation strategies to solve number problems including those involving money and measures? (Ma2 Level 2) ❑

- Do the children choose the appropriate operation when solving addition and subtraction problems? Do they use repeated addition to solve multiplication problems? Are they beginning to use repeated subtraction or sharing equally to solve division problems? Can they solve number problems involving money and measures? (Ma2 Level 2) ☐

- Do they record their work in writing, eg record their mental calculations as number sentences? (Ma2 Level 2) ☐

Shape, space and measures

Pupils use mathematical names for common 3-D and 2-D shapes and describe their properties, including numbers of sides and corners. They distinguish between straight and turning movements, understand angles as a measure of turn, and recognise right angles in turns. They begin to use everyday non-standard and standard units to measure length and mass.

- Do the children use mathematical names for common 3-D and 2-D shapes, eg square, triangle, hexagon, pentagon, octagon, cube, cylinder, sphere, cuboid, pyramid? Do they describe their properties, including numbers of sides and corners? Do they make and talk about shapes referring to features and properties using language such as edge, face, corner? Do they sort 2-D and 3-D shapes according to a single criterion? Can they visualise frequently used 2-D and 3-D shapes? Are they beginning to understand the difference between shapes with two dimension and those with three? Do they recognise the properties that are the same even when a shape is enlarged? (Ma3 Level 2) ☐

- Can the children describe the position of objects, eg by using ordinal numbers (first, second, third, …)? Do they recognise that a shape stays the same even when it is held up in different orientations? Can they distinguish between straight and turning movements, eg between left and right and between clockwise and anticlockwise? Do they recognise right angles in turns? (Ma3 Level 2) ☐

- Do the children understand angle as a measure of turn, making whole turns, half turns and quarter turns? Are they beginning to use everyday non-standard and standard units to measure length and mass? Do they understand that numbers can be used to describe continuous measures? Do they know which measuring tools to use? Are they beginning to use a wider range of measures, eg a right angle checker or a time line? (Ma3 Level 2) ☐

Handling data

Pupils sort objects and classify them using more than one criterion. When they have gathered information, pupils record results in simple lists, tables and block graphs, in order to communicate their findings.

- Do the children sort objects and classify them using more than one criterion, eg sort a set of shapes using two criteria such as triangle/not triangle and blue/not blue? Do they understand the vocabulary related to handling data, such as 'sort', 'group', 'set', 'list', 'table', 'most common', 'most popular'? Can they collect and sort data to test a simple hypothesis? Can they record results in simple lists, tables, pictograms and block graphs? (Ma4 Level 2) ☐

- Can the children communicate their findings, using the simple lists, tables, pictograms and block graphs they have recorded, eg by responding to questions about the data they have presented and posing similar questions for others to answer? (Ma4 Level 2) ☐

Name ______________________ Date ____________

Sheet 1

How can we count the butterflies?

Teacher's notes

Suggested objective: ***Estimate and check a number by counting.***

Problem: ***How can we count the butterflies? We don't want to miss any out. We only want to count each one once.***

Look at the butterflies. Encourage the children to say how many they think there are – you could write down their estimates and explain that it doesn't matter if they haven't found exactly the right number.

They may suggest marking each butterfly in some way, or matching each butterfly to a counter, or a different method completely. What's important is that they should be able to suggest a strategy. Once they have done so, see if they can follow it through successfully.

Name ______________________ Date ____________

Sheet 2

How can we count the cats?

Teacher's notes

Suggested objective: ***Estimate and check a number by counting.***

Problem: ***How can we count the cats? We don't want to miss any out. We only want to count each one once.***

Look at the cats. Encourage the children to say how many they think there are. They may suggest marking each cat in some way, or matching each cat to a counter, or a different method completely. What's important is that they should be able to suggest a strategy. Once they have done so, see if they can follow it through successfully.

Name ______________________ Date ____________

Sheet 3

How can we count the animals?

Teacher's notes

Suggested objective: ***Estimate and check a number by counting.***

Problem: ***How can we count the animals?***
Look at the animals. Encourage the children to say how many they think there are. Does anybody suggest counting in twos? Allow the children to make suggestions, helping them to realise that there may be several ways of counting the animals. Does anybody suggest counting in twos? You may wish to suggest this strategy but not all children will find this easy to understand.

Name ______________________ Date ____________

Sheet 4

How can we sort the animals?

Teacher's notes

This activity sheet to be used in conjunction with Sheets 5 and 6.

Suggested objective: ***Estimate and check a number by counting in twos.***

Problem: ***How can we sort the animals to go on the ark?***

Ask the children to cut out the individual animals and sort them into pairs, then to stick them on the ark on Sheet 4. Encourage them to use the vocabulary: above, below, side, on, in, in front, behind, next to, between. How many pairs are there? How many animals are there altogether?

Name ______________________ Date ______________

How can we sort the animals?

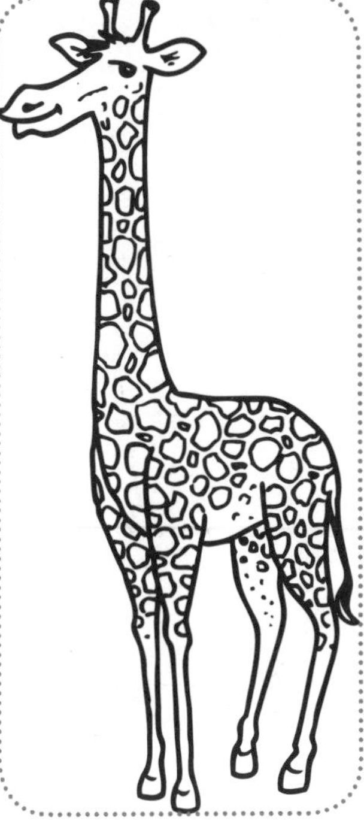

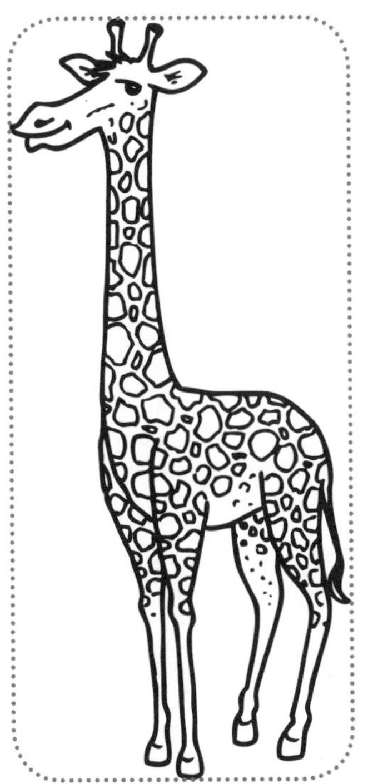

Teacher's notes

This activity sheet to be used in conjunction with Sheets 4 and 6.
Suggested objective: ***Estimate and check a number by counting in twos.***

Problem: ***How can we sort the animals to go on the ark?***
Ask the children to cut out the individual animals and sort them into pairs, then stick them on the ark on Sheet 4. Encourage them to use the vocabulary: above, below, side, on, in, in front, behind, next to, between. How many pairs are there? How many animals are there altogether?

Name ______________________ Date __________

Sheet 6

How can we sort the animals?

Teacher's notes

This activity sheet to be used in conjunction with Sheets 4 and 5.

Suggested objective: ***Estimate and check a number by counting in twos.***

Problem: ***How can we sort the animals to go on the ark? Will they all fit?***

Name ______________________ Date ____________

What will you buy at the pound shop?

Sheet 7

You have £5 to spend.

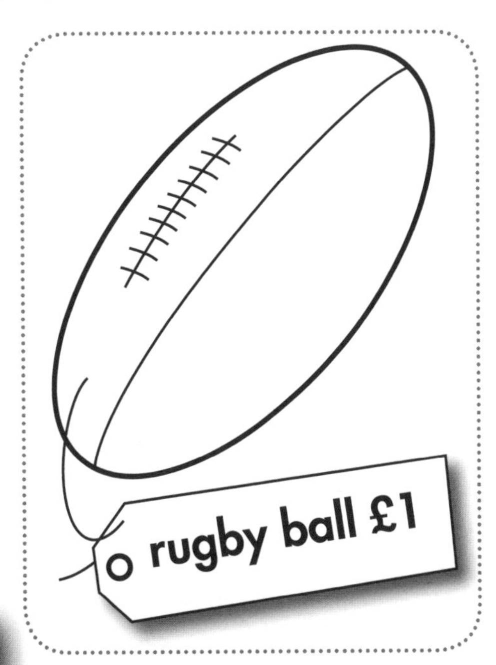

Teacher's notes

This activity sheet to be used in conjunction with Sheet 9.
Suggested objective: ***Solve problems involving £1 coins.***

Problem: ***You have £5 to spend. What will you buy?***
Will you have any money left? How much? Ask the children to cut out the items separately and stick their choice of shopping on the recording chart on Sheet 9. To make the problem more challenging, you could print and cut out more than one copy of each item.

Name ______________________________ Date ______________

Sheet 8

What will you buy at the pound shop?

You have £5 to spend.

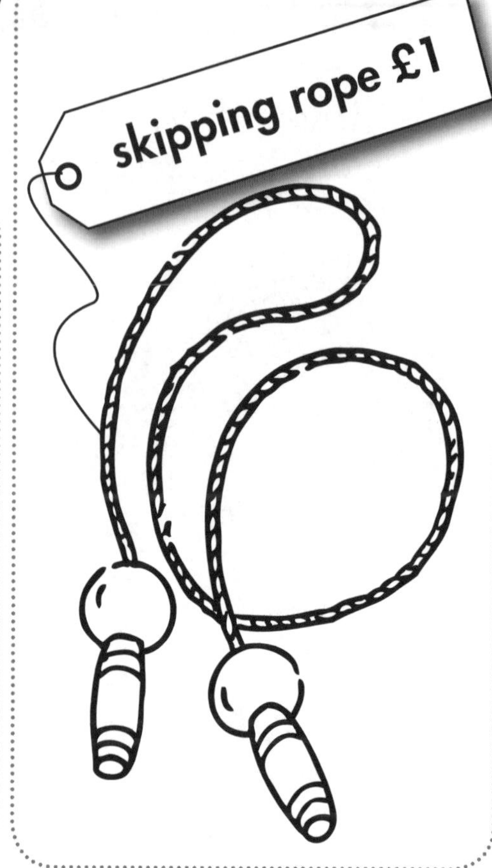

Teacher's notes

This activity sheet to be used in conjunction with Sheet 9.
Suggested objective: ***Solve problems involving £1 coins.***

Problem: ***You have £5 to spend. What will you buy?***
Will you have any money left? How much? Ask the children to cut out the items separately and stick their choice of shopping on the recording chart on Sheet 9. To make the problem more challenging, you could print and cut out more than one copy of each item.

Name ______________________ Date __________

What did you buy at the pound shop?

I had £5.     

I bought

I spent £ [ ]

I have £ [ ] left.

Teacher's notes

This activity sheet to be used in conjunction with Sheets 7 and 8.
Suggested objective: ***Solve problems involving £1 coins.***

Problem: ***You had £5 to spend. What did you buy?***
What did you buy at the pound shop? Did you have any money left? How much? Once the children have decided what they will buy at the pound shop, give them a copy of this sheet so that they can record their shopping by either drawing the items or sticking them on.

Name ______________________ Date ____________

What does Meg need to buy?

Sheet 10

Meg wants to do some decorating.
She has £10 to spend.
What items does she need from the Pound Shop?

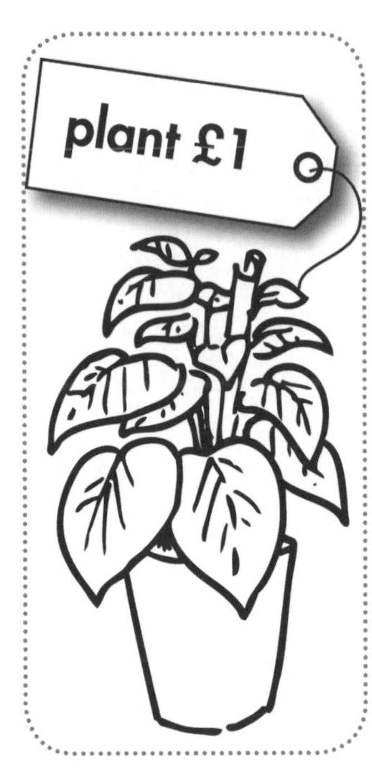

Teacher's notes

This activity sheet to be used in conjunction with Sheet 11.
Suggested objective: ***Solve addition and subtraction problems involving £1 coins.***

Problem: ***Meg wants to do some decorating.*** What items does she need from the Pound Shop? How much will they cost her altogether? What change will she have from £10? What could she do with her change? Ask the children to cut out the items and choose what Meg should buy.

Name ______________________ Date ____________

What did Meg buy for decorating?

Sheet 11

How much did Meg spend? £

Meg had £10. How much has she got left? £

Teacher's notes

This activity sheet to be used in conjunction with Sheet 10.
Suggested objective: ***Solve addition and subtraction problems involving £1 coins.***

Problem: ***Meg wants to do some decorating. What items does she need from the Pound Shop?*** How much will they cost her altogether? What change will she have from £10? What could she do with her change? Once the children have made their selection, ask them to either draw or stick the cut out pictures of the shopping on this sheet.

Name ______________________ Date ____________

Sheet 12

What does Ted need to buy?

Ted wants to do some gardening.
He has £10 to spend.
What items does he need from the Pound Shop?

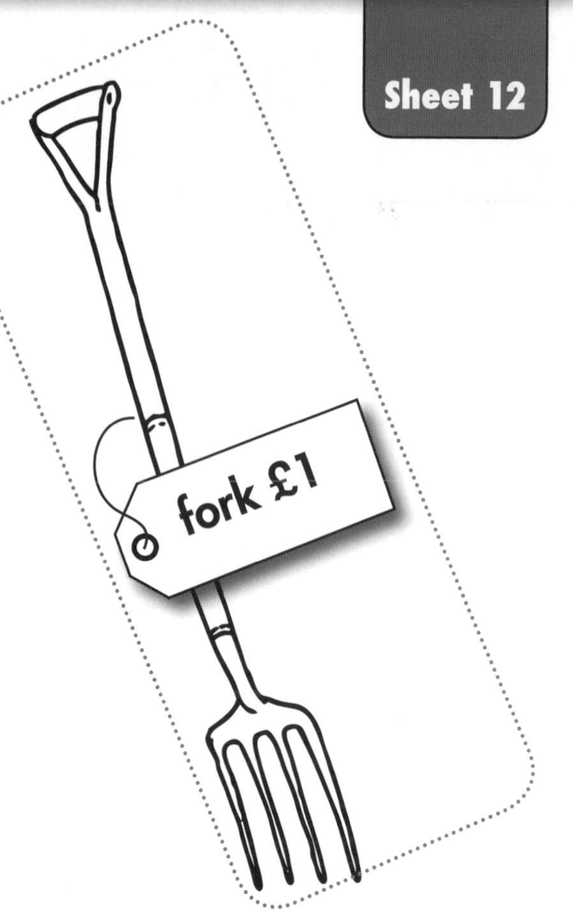

Teacher's notes

This activity sheet to be used in conjunction with Sheet 13.
Suggested objective: ***Solve addition and subtraction problems involving £1 coins.***

Problem: ***Ted wants to do some gardening.*** What items does he need from the Pound Shop? How much will they cost him altogether? What change will he have from £10? What could he do with his change? Ask the chidren to cut out the items and choose what Ted should buy.

Name ________________________ Date ____________

What did Ted buy for gardening?

Sheet 13

How much did Ted spend? £

Ted had £10. How much has he got left? £

Teacher's notes

This activity sheet to be used in conjunction with Sheet 11.
Suggested objective: ***Solve addition and subtraction problems involving £1 coins.***

Problem: ***Ted wants to do some gardening. What items does he need from the Pound Shop?***
How much will they cost him altogether? What change will he have from £10? What could he do with his change? Once the children have made their selection, ask them to either draw or stick the cut out pictures of the shopping on this sheet.
Extension Problem: ***Look at both Meg and Ted's shopping. Who spent more, Meg or Ted?***

Name ______________________ Date ____________

What clothes will you buy for Tom?

Sheet 14

You have £10 to spend.

Teacher's notes

This activity sheet to be used in conjunction with Sheets 15 and 18.

Suggested objective: ***Solve addition and subtraction problems involving £1 coins.***

Problem: ***What clothes will you buy Tom? You have £10 to spend. How much will they cost altogether? How much money will you have left?***

Ask the children to cut out the clothes and choose what they will buy for Tom. (You could photocopy and cut out extra copies of the clothes so that the children can use these for recording their shopping on Sheet 18.)

Extension problem: ***Compare the prices of the clothes.***

Which is the most expensive item? Which is the cheapest item? Which things cost the same? How much more are the trousers than the shorts?

Name ______________________________ Date ______________

Sheet 15

What clothes will you buy for Tom?

You have £10 to spend.

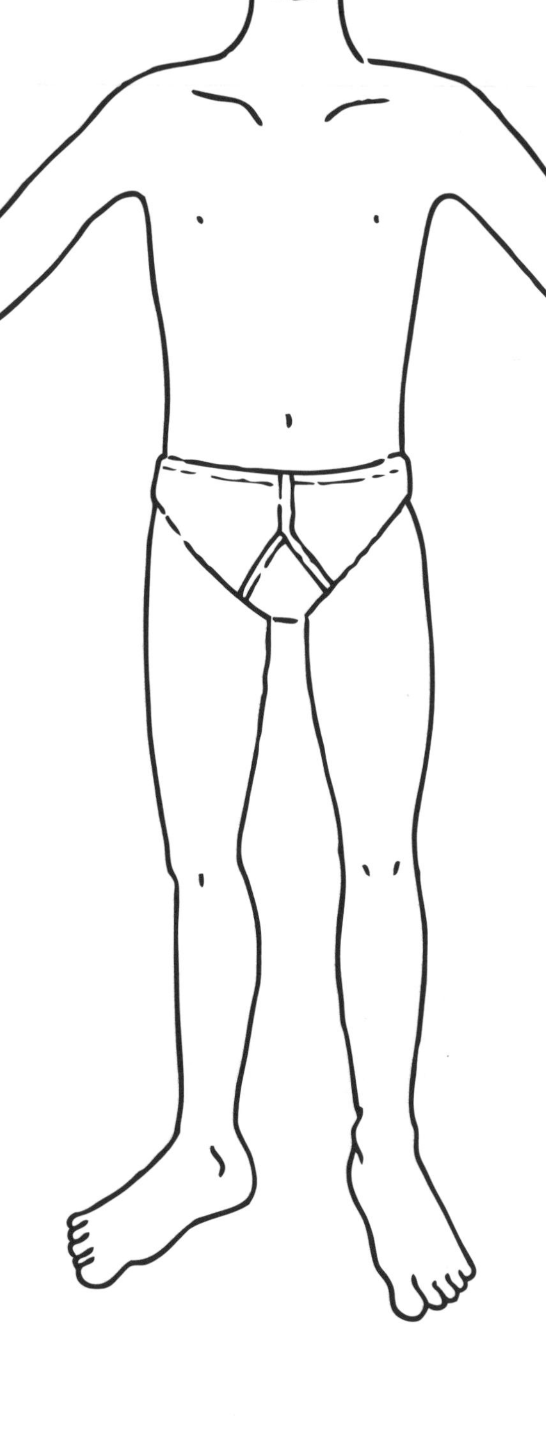

Teacher's notes

This activity sheet to be used in conjunction with Sheets 14 and 18.

Suggested objective:
Solve addition and subtraction problems involving £1 coins.

Problem: ***You have £10 to spend.*** What clothes can you buy to dress Tom? How much will they cost altogether? How much money will you have left? Ask the children to choose and cut out clothes for Tom (from Sheet 14) and stick them on him.

Name ______________________ Date ____________

What clothes will you buy for Ruby?

You have £10 to spend.

Teacher's notes

This activity sheet to be used in conjunction with Sheets 17 and 18.
Suggested objective: ***Solve addition and subtraction problems involving £1 coins.***

Problem: ***What clothes will you buy Ruby? You have £10 to spend. How much will they cost altogether? How much money have you got left?***
Ask the children to cut out the clothes and choose what they will buy for Ruby. (You could photocopy and cut out extra copies of the clothes so that the children can use these for recording on Sheet 18).
Extension problem: ***Compare the prices of the clothes.***
Which is the most expensive item? Which is the cheapest item? Which things cost the same? How much more is the dress than the skirt?

Name ______________________ Date ______________

What clothes will you buy for Ruby?

You have £10 to spend.

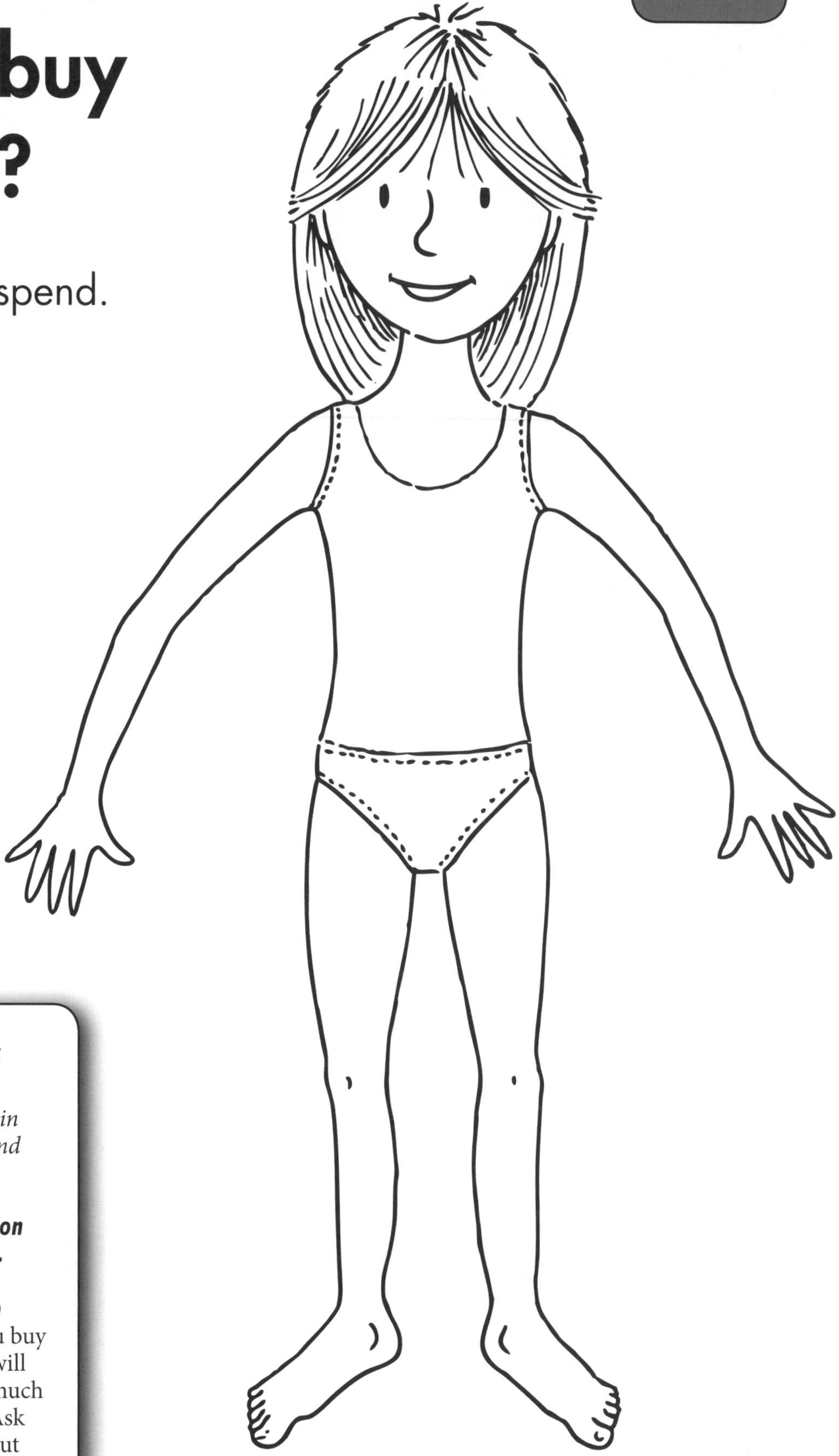

Teacher's notes

This activity sheet to be used in conjunction with Sheets 16 and 18.

Suggested objective:
Solve addition and subtraction problems involving £1 coins.

Problem: ***You have £10 to spend.*** What clothes can you buy to dress Ruby? How much will they cost altogether? How much money will you have left? Ask the children to choose and cut out clothes for Ruby (from Sheet 16) and stick them on her.

Name ______________________ Date ______________

What did you buy at the clothes shop?

Sheet 18

I had £10.

I bought

I spent £

I have £ left.

Teacher's notes

This activity sheet to be used in conjunction with Sheet 14-17.

Suggested objective: ***Solve addition and subtraction problems involving £1 coins.***

Problem: ***You had £10 to spend. What did you buy at the clothes shop?***

Did you have any money left? How much? Once the children have decided what they will spend at the clothes shop, give them a copy of this sheet so that they can record their shopping.

Shape

Teacher's notes

The following sheets are about Shape. Photocopy each of the Shape sheets, 19 to 26, laminate each sheet and cut out all the shapes accurately, giving you the following shapes:

- 2 big squares: one spotty, one stripy
- 6 small squares: two spotty, two shaded, two stripy
- 3 big rectangles: one spotty, one shaded, one stripy
- 6 small rectangles: two spotty, two shaded, two stripy
- 3 big triangles: one spotty, one shaded, one stripy
- 6 small triangles: two spotty, two shaded, two stripy
- 2 big circles: one spotty, one stripy
- 6 small circles: two spotty, two shaded, two stripy

Working with the cut-out shapes will address several key aspects of maths: Using and applying, Understanding shape, Measuring and Handling Data.

Suggested problems to promote discussion and investigation:

- How many small squares will fit exactly on a large square?
- How many large rectangles will fit exactly on a large square?
- How many small rectangles will fit exactly on a large square?
- How many small squares will fit exactly on a large rectangle?
- How many small rectangles will fit exactly on a large rectangle?
- How many small triangles will fit exactly on a large triangle?
- Can you make the triangles fit exactly on to any other shape?
- Can you make the circles fit exactly on to any other shape?
- Can you sort the shapes into groups?
  Eg, large shapes/small shapes, Spotty shapes/other shapes, Shapes that are large and spotty/all the other shapes, Shapes that have four sides/shapes that don't have four sides, Shapes that have corners/shapes that don't have corners

Using the shapes you will cover the following objectives:

- Engage with practical activities involving sorting, counting and measuring by direct comparison.
- Represent work with objects or pictures.
- Discuss and compare shapes.
- Describe the different ways that shapes have been sorted.
- Use everyday language to describe properties of 2-D shapes.
- Sort shapes and say how they have been selected.
- Use properties such as large, small, stack.
- Use everyday language to describe positions of 2-D shapes.
- Respond to and use positional language.
- Sort and classify objects using one criterion or two criteria.
- Sort the shapes using a large scale Venn diagram (or Carroll diagram).
- Represent work by using the objects that have been sorted.
- Respond to questions about how objects have been sorted and why each object belongs in a set.

Big squares

Small squares

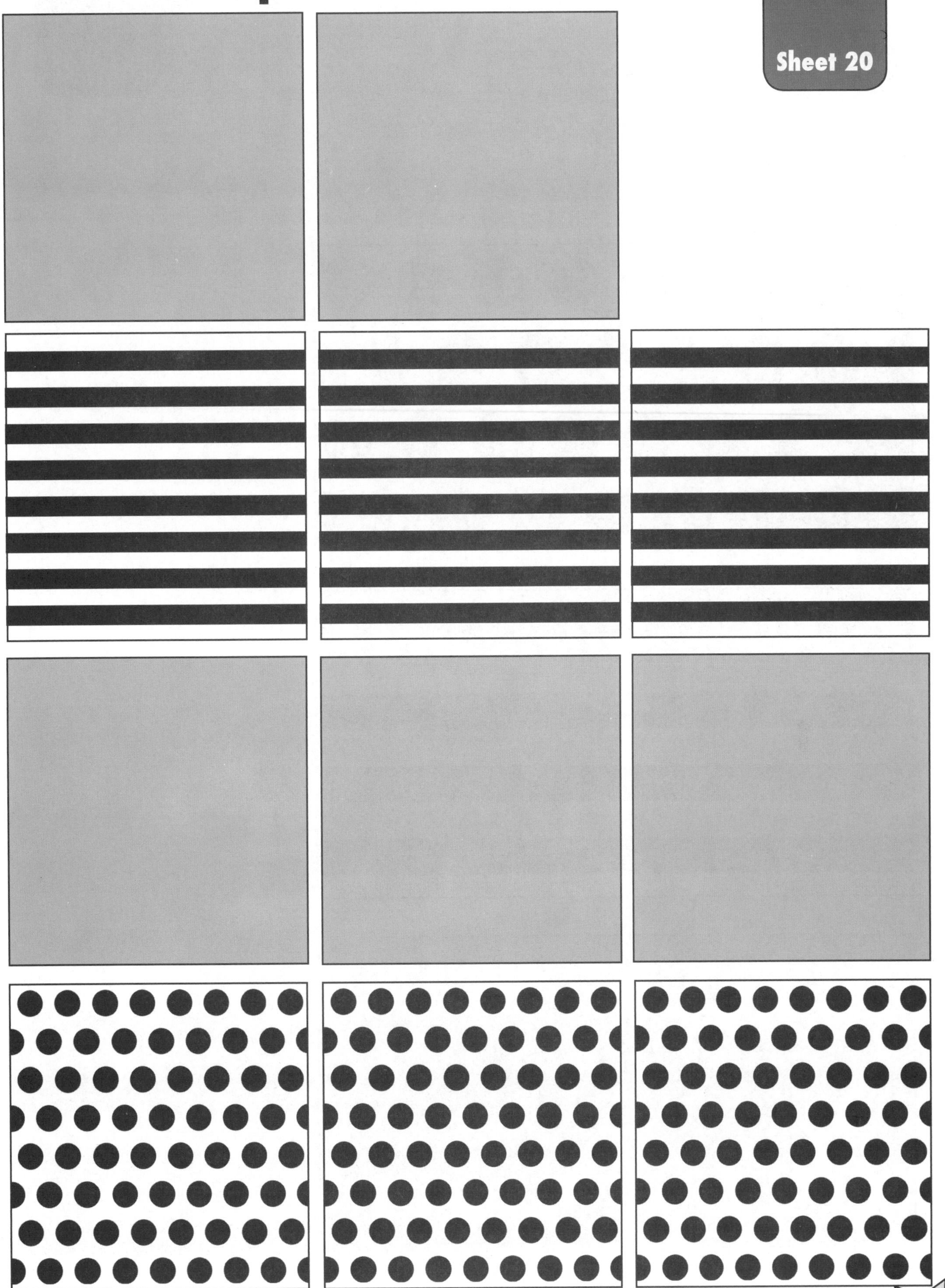

Big rectangles

Small rectangles

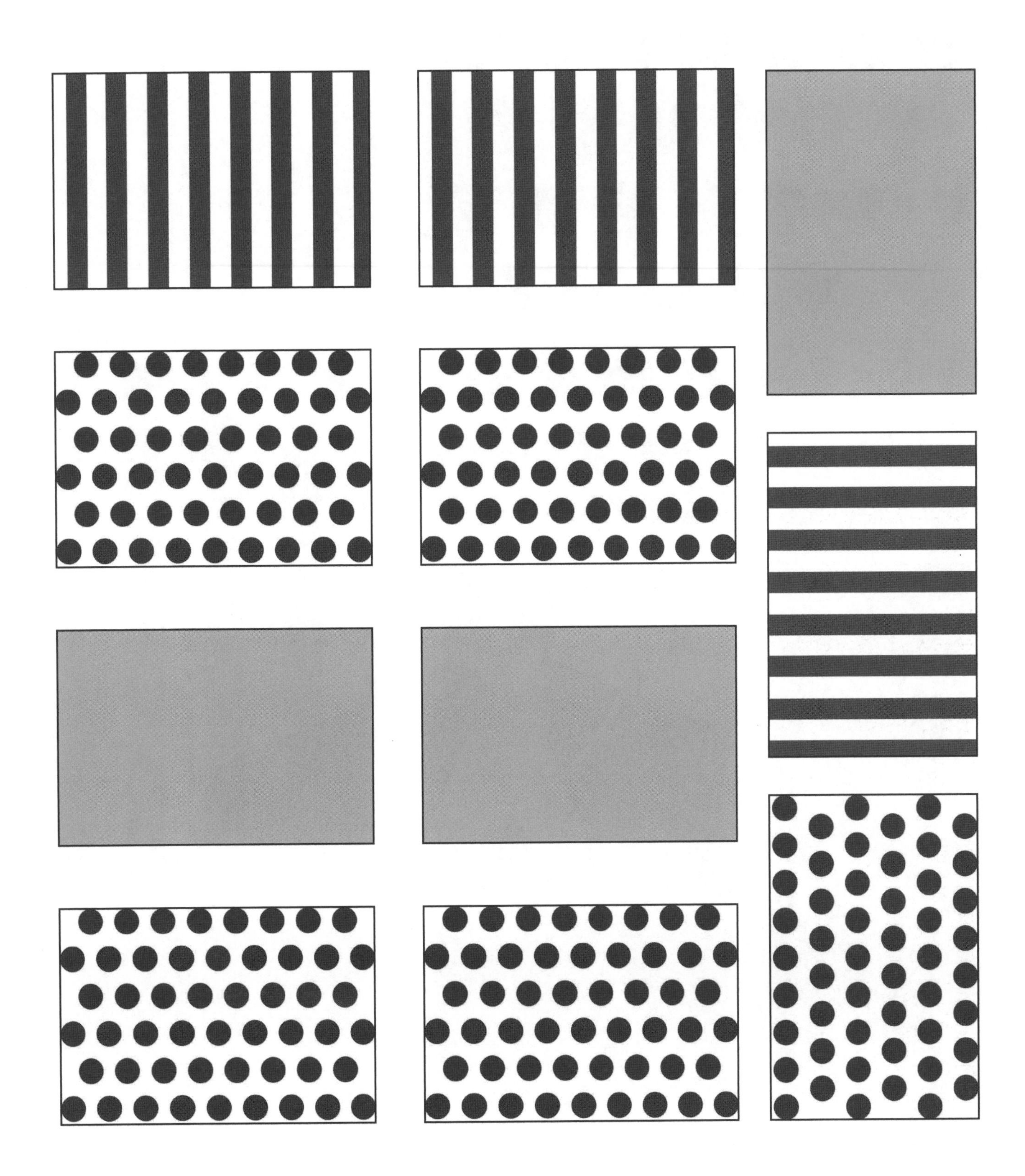

Big triangles

Small triangles

Sheet 24

Big circles

Small circles

Sheet 26

Name ______________________ Date __________

Can you sort the shapes?

Sheet 27

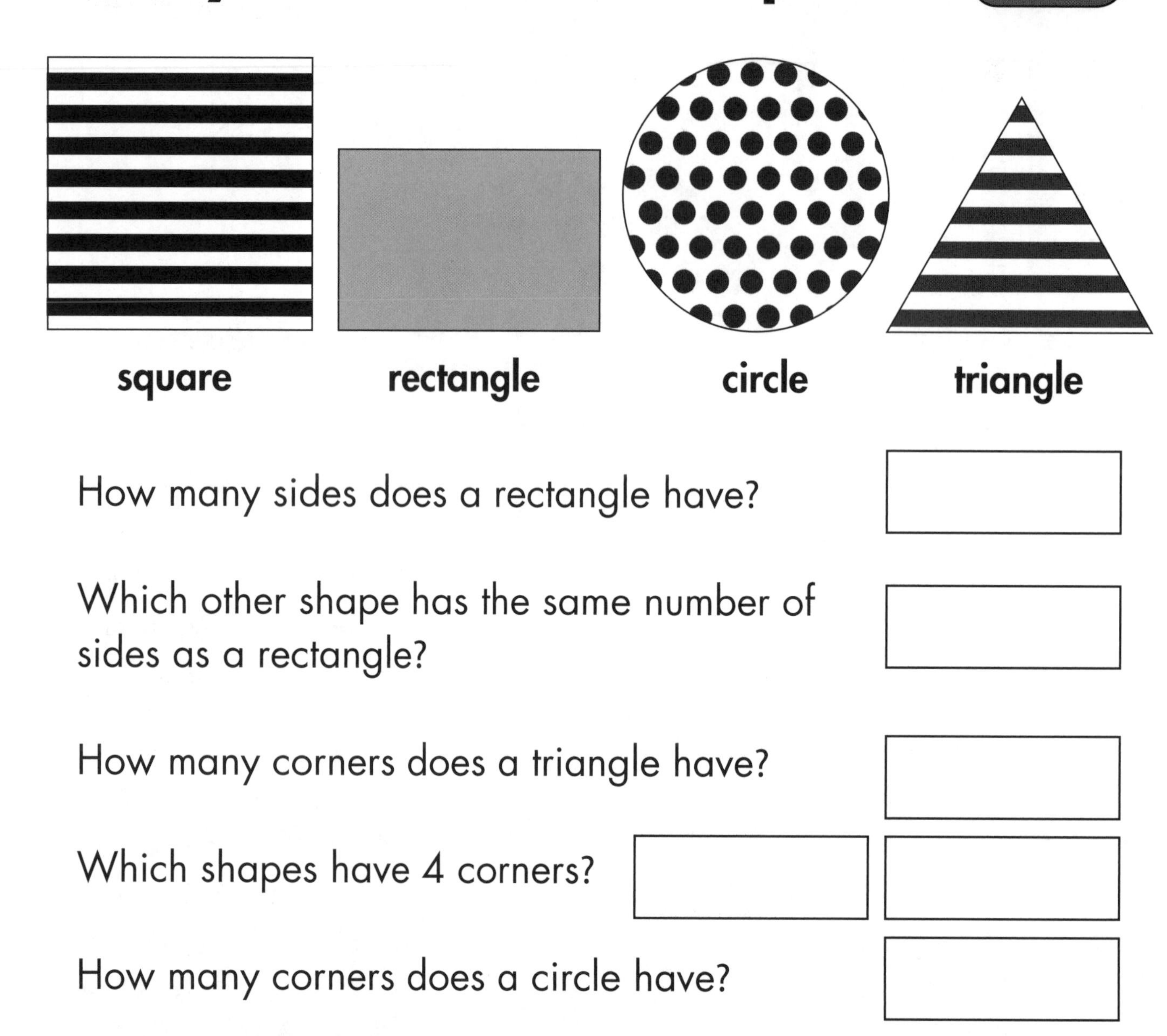

How many sides does a rectangle have? [ ]

Which other shape has the same number of sides as a rectangle? [ ]

How many corners does a triangle have? [ ]

Which shapes have 4 corners? [ ] [ ]

How many corners does a circle have? [ ]

Teacher's notes

This activity sheet to be used in conjunction with Sheet 19-26.
Suggested objective: ***Refer to features of shapes, such as sides and corners.***

Problem: ***Can you sort the shapes?***
Give the children the set of shapes that have been cut out from Sheets 19 to 26, then present them with the problem of how to sort them. The questions on this sheet are designed to give clues for dealing with this problem. You could give them a large scale Venn diagram or Carroll diagram to help with the sorting. If possible, encourage them to come up with ideas for sorting, though you could make some suggestions: large shapes/small shapes; spotty shapes/other shapes; shapes that are large and spotty/all the other shapes; shapes that have four sides/shapes that don't have four sides; shapes that have corners/shapes that don't have corners. Note that the final question can be very confusing for some children, as they are not accustomed to answering with zero.

Name ______________________________ *Date* ______________

Which bear is taller?

Sheet 28

Teacher's notes

Suggested objective: ***Measure using direct comparison.***

Problem: Which ***bear is taller? How can you find out?***
Ask the children to cut out each bear. Children may choose to solve this problem by simply comparing the heights of the two cut-out bears, and later the four bears (See Sheet 30) – this is probably the best way to address the problem and they should be praised for suggesting it.

Extension problem: Ask the children to use non-standard units or standard units to measure the height of each bear. This is a much more difficult concept as they now have to compare the numbers represented by the measurements.

Name ______________________ Date ____________

Can you measure the bears?

Sheet 29

Teacher's notes

Suggested objective: ***Measure and order using direct comparison.***

Problem: ***How tall are Kim and Pam? How can you find out?***
Ask the children to cut out each bear and measure them with standard units.

Name ______________________ Date ____________

How tall are the bears?

Sheet 30

Name of bear	Height
Ted	
Ned	
Kim	
Pam	

Which bear is the tallest? [ ]

Which bear is the shortest? [ ]

Write the names of the bears in order of height.

[ ] [ ] [ ] [ ]

Teacher's notes

This activity sheet to be used in conjunction with Sheet 28-29.

Suggested objective: ***Measure and order using direct comparison.***

Problems: ***How tall are the bears? Which is the tallest bear? Which is the shortest bear?***
Once the children have measured the cut-out bears on Sheets 28 and 29, ask them to record their findings on this sheet and answer the questions.

Extension problem: ***Can you measure the bears accurately in centimetres?***
This problem is suitable for children who are beginning to gain confidence in measuring with standard units. Can they measure the bears accurately using centimetres?

Name ______________________________ Date ______________

Which car is longer?

Sheet 31

Teacher's notes

Suggested objective: ***Measure and order using direct comparison.***

Problem: ***Which car is longer? How can you find out?***
Children might choose to solve this problem by simply comparing the lengths of the two cars (and later the four cars), this is probably the best way to address the problem and they should be praised for suggesting it.
Extension problem: Ask the children to use non-standard units or standard units to measure the length of each car. This is a much more difficult concept as they now have to compare the numbers represented by the measurements.

Name ______________________ Date __________

Can you measure the cars?

Sheet 32

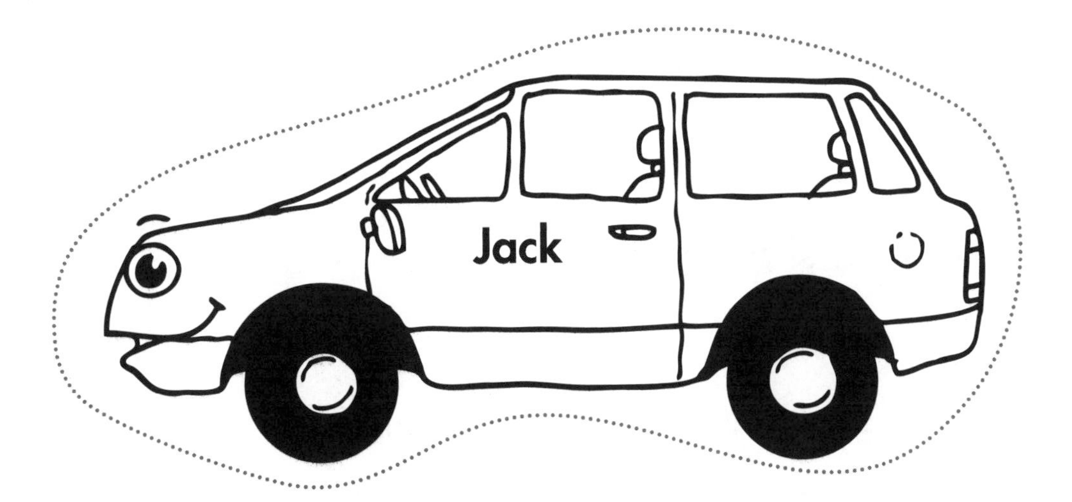

Teacher's notes

Suggested objective: ***Measure and order using direct comparison.***

Problem: ***Which car is longer? How can you find out?***
Children might choose to solve this problem by simply comparing the lengths of the two cars (and later the four cars), this is probably the best way to address the problem and they should be praised for suggesting it.
Extension problem: Ask the children to use non-standard units or standard units to measure the length of each car. This is a much more difficult concept as they now have to compare the numbers represented by the measurements.

Name ______________________ Date ____________

How long are the cars?

Sheet 33

Name of car	Length
Dolly	
Robbie	
Sarah	
Jack	

Which car is the longest? [ ]

Which car is the shortest? [ ]

Write the names of the cars in order of length.

[ ] [ ] [ ] [ ]

Teacher's notes

Suggested objective: ***Measure and order using direct comparison.***

Problems: ***Hoe big are the cars?***

Once the children have measured the cut-out cars on Sheets 31 and 32, ask them to record their findings on this sheet. Which is the longest car? Which is the shortest car?

This problem is suitable for children who are beginning to gain confidence in measuring with standard units. Can they measure the cars accurately using centimetres?

Name ______________________ Date ____________

Sheet 34

Can you put the days in order?

Saturday

Thursday

Monday

Wednesday

Sunday

Tuesday

Friday

Teacher's notes

This activity sheet to be used in conjunction with Sheet 35.
Suggested objective: ***Use the vocabulary of time for days of the week.***

Problems: ***Can you put the days of the week in the correct order?***
Which days are at the weekend? What day is it today? What day was it yesterday? What day will it be tomorrow? Cut out the separate days of the week and put them into the correct order.
This activity offers the opportunity to extend vocabulary in relation to time, using terms such as before, after, next, first, last.

Name ______________________ Date ____________

Can you put the days in order?

Teacher's notes

This activity sheet to be used in conjunction with Sheet 34.

Suggested objective: ***Use the vocabulary of time for days of the week.***

Problem: ***Can you put the days of the week in the correct order?***

Here the children need to refer to their own prior knowledge or to an existing chart showing days of the week. Using the cut-out days of the week from Sheet 34, ask the children to stick the names onto this sheet in the correct order, using vocabulary such as above, below, before, after.

Name ______________________ Date __________

What day is it?

Sheet 36

What day is it today? [ ]

What day was it yesterday? [ ]

What day will it be tomorrow? [ ]

What day is the one before Sunday? [ ]

What day is the one after Monday? [ ]

Which days are at the weekend? [ ]

[ ]

Teacher's notes

Suggested objective: ***Use the vocabulary of time for days of the week.***

Problems: Children answer the questions above. They will need to use their own prior knowledge or to refer to the chart that they have completed on sheet 35. In observing them dealing with the questions you are able to assess several aspects of the Assessment Focuses for Using and Applying Mathematics and for Shape, Space and Measures at Level 1: Do the children respond to questions? Do they refer to materials they have used? Do they use the vocabulary of time, such as before, after, today, tomorrow, yesterday, weekend?

Name ______________________ Date ______________

Sheet 37

Can you put the months in order?

February	October	August
May	January	September
November	June	April
March	December	July

Teacher's notes

This activity sheet to be used in conjunction with Sheet 38.
Suggested objective: ***Use the vocabulary of time for months of the year.***

Problems: ***Can you put the months of the year in the correct order?***
Which months are in the summer? What month is it now? What month was it last month? What will next month be? Children cut out the months of the year and arrange them in the correct order on Sheet 38. This activity offers a further opportunity to extend vocabulary in relation to time, using terms such as before, after, next, first, last. More able pupils might also be able to respond to questions involving all the ordinal numbers from 'first' to 'twelfth'.

Name ______________________ Date ____________

Sheet 38

Can you put the months in order?

Teacher's notes

This activity sheet to be used in conjunction with Sheet 37.
Suggested objective: ***Use the vocabulary of time for months of the year.***

Problem: ***Can you put the months in order?***
Using the cut-out months of the year from Sheet 37, ask the children to stick the names onto this sheet in the correct order going from left to right on the grid. This activity offers a further opportunity to extend vocabulary in relation to time, using terms such as before, after, next, first, last. More able pupils might also be able to respond to questions involving all the ordinal numbers from 'first' to 'twelfth'.

Name ______________________ Date __________

What month is it?

Sheet 39

What month is it now?

What month was it last month?

What month will next month be?

In what month is your birthday?

What month is the one after February?

What month is the one before June?

Teacher's notes

Suggested objective: ***Use the vocabulary of time for months of the year.***

Problems: Children answer the questions above. They will need to use their own prior knowledge or to refer to the chart that they have created, which shows months of the year in order. In observing them dealing with the questions you are able to assess several aspects of the Assessment Focuses for Using and Applying Mathematics and for Shape, Space and Measures at Level 1: Do the children respond to questions? Do they refer to materials they have used? Do they use the vocabulary of time, such as before, after, next, last, first, second, etc?

Name ______________________ Date ______________

How many more toy cars does Ben need?

Teacher's notes

This activity sheet to be used in conjunction with Sheets 41, 42 and 43. Each sheet can be used separately as a prompt for discussing problems. Use all three sheets together for Sheet 43.

Suggested objective: ***Solve addition and subtraction problems involving up to 10 objects.***

Problem: ***How many more toy cars does Ben need to have five? How many more would he need to have ten?***

This activity extends thinking in relation to number. Most children will need some apparatus to help them work out the problems so it would be very helpful to have some toy cars available for them to use.

Name ______________________________ Date ______________

How many more toy cars does Kara need?

Sheet 41

Teacher's notes

This activity sheet to be used in conjunction with Sheets 40, 42 and 43. Each sheet can be used separately as a prompt for discussing problems. Use all three sheets together for Sheet 43.

Suggested objective: ***Solve addition and subtraction problems involving up to 10 objects.***

Problem: ***How many toy cars does Kara have? How many more than five has she got? How many more would she need to have ten?***

This activity extends thinking in relation to number. Most children will need some apparatus to help them to work out the problems so it would be very helpful to have some toy cars available for them to use.

Name ______________________ Date ____________

Sheet 42

How many more toy cars does Ali need?

Teacher's notes

This activity sheet to be used in conjunction with Sheets 40, 41 and 43. Each sheet can be used separately as a prompt for discussing problems. Use all three sheets together for Sheet 43.

Suggested objective: ***Solve addition and subtraction problems involving up to 10 objects.***

Problem: ***How many toy cars does Ali have? How many more than five has he got? How many more would he need to have ten?***

This activity extends thinking in relation to number. Most children will need some apparatus to help them to work out the problems so it would be very helpful to have some toy cars available for them to use. Does the child have an effective strategy for counting the cars?

Name ______________________ Date __________

Sheet 43

Questions about the toy cars

How many cars has Ben got? [ ]

How many cars has Kara got? [ ]

How many cars has Ali got? [ ]

Who has the most cars? [ ]

How many more than Ben does Ali have? [ ]

How many more than Ben does Kara have? [ ]

Teacher's notes

This activity sheet to be used in conjunction with Sheets 40, 41 and 42.
Suggested objective: ***Solve addition and subtraction problems involving up to 10 objects.***

Problems: Children answer the questions above. They will need to interpret each question, particularly those comparing the numbers of cars.

Name ______________________ Date ____________

Sheet 44

What time is it?

Word bank

o'clock one two three four five six seven eight nine ten eleven twelve

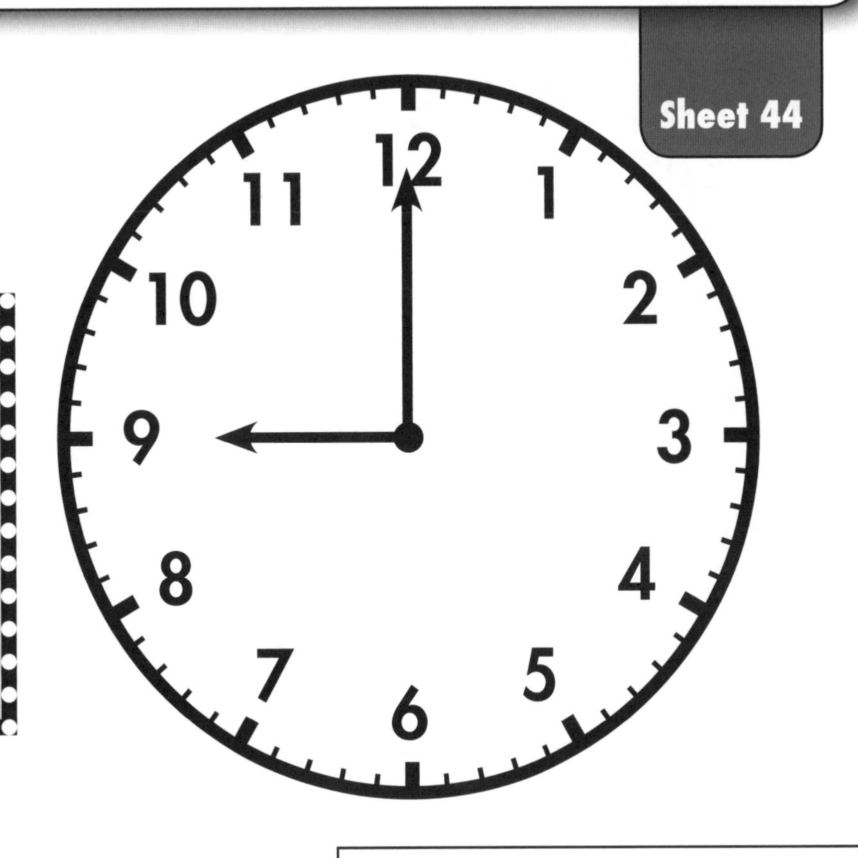

What time does the clock show? [ ]

What time will it be one hour later? [ ]

What time will it be two hours later? [ ]

What time will it be three hours later? [ ]

Teacher's notes

Suggested objective: ***Solve problems about time.***

Problems: Children answer the questions above. They will need to interpret the questions, understanding the vocabulary of time. It would be a good idea to have a geared clock for them to use. Ensure that the children understand that each question refers to the original time shown on the clock.

Name ______________________ Date ______________

Sheet 45

What time will it be?

Word bank

o'clock one two three four five six seven eight nine ten eleven twelve

What time does the clock show? [ ]

What time will it be two hours later? [ ]

What time will it be five hours later? [ ]

How many hours will it be until it's five o'clock? [ ]

Teacher's notes

Suggested objective: ***Solve problems about time.***

Problems: Children answer the questions above. They will need to interpret the questions, understanding the vocabulary of time. It would be a good idea to have a geared clock for them to use. Ensure that the children understand that each question refers to the original time shown on the clock.

Name ______________________ Date ____________

Sheet 46

What time will it be?

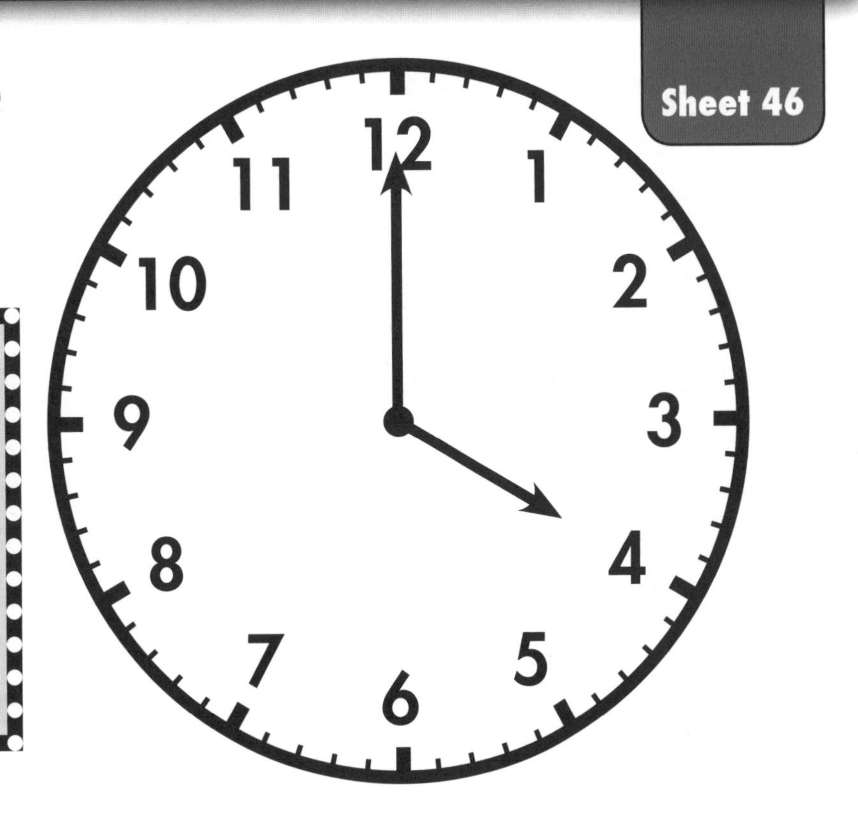

Word bank

o'clock one two three four five six seven eight nine ten eleven twelve

What time does the clock show? [ ]

What time will it be four hours later? [ ]

What time will it be six hours later? [ ]

How many hours will it be until it's 9 o'clock? [ ]

Teacher's notes

Suggested objective: ***Solve problems about time.***

Problems: Children answer the questions above. They will need to interpret the questions, understanding the vocabulary of time. It would be a good idea to have a geared clock for them to use. Ensure that the children understand that each question refers to the original time shown on the clock.

Name ______________________ Date ______________

What time was it?

Word bank

o'clock one two three four five six seven eight nine ten eleven twelve

What time does the clock show? [ ]

What time was it one hour before this time? [ ]

What time was it three hours before this time? [ ]

How long after 3 o'clock is this time? [ ]

Teacher's notes

Suggested objective: ***Solve problems about time.***

Problems: Children answer the questions above. They will need to interpret the questions, understanding the vocabulary of time. It would be a good idea to have a geared clock for them to use. Ensure that the children understand that each question refers to the original time shown on the clock.

Name ______________________________ Date ______________

Sheet 48

What time was it?

Word bank

o'clock one two three four five six seven eight nine ten eleven twelve

What time does the clock show? [ ]

What time was it one hour before this time? [ ]

What time was it four hours before this time? [ ]

How long after 9 o'clock is this time? [ ]

Teacher's notes

Suggested objective: ***Solve problems about time.***

Problems: Children to answer the questions above. They will need to interpret the questions, understanding the vocabulary of time. It would be a good idea to have a geared clock for them to use. Ensure that the children understand that each question refers to the original time shown on the clock.

Name ______________________ Date ____________

What time will it be?

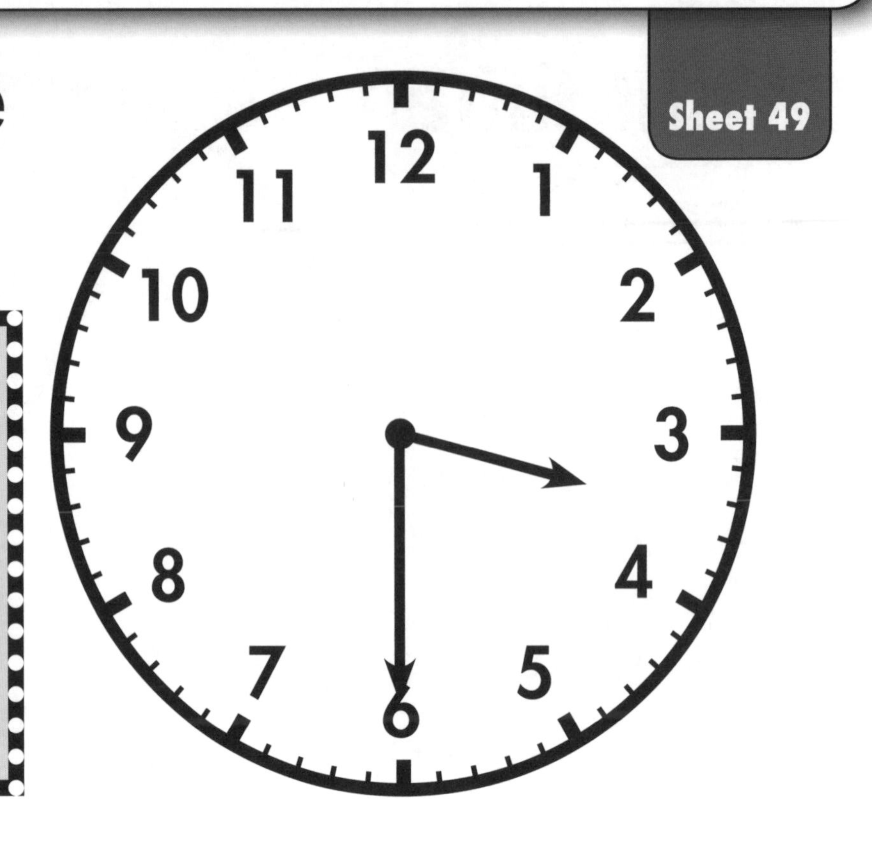

Word bank

o'clock half past
one two three four
five six seven eight
nine ten eleven
twelve

What time does the clock show? [ ]

What time will it be one hour later? [ ]

What time will it be two hours later? [ ]

What time will it be three hours later? [ ]

Teacher's notes

Suggested objective: ***Solve problems about half past.***

Problems: Children answer the questions above. They will need to interpret the questions, understanding the vocabulary of time. It would be a good idea to have a geared clock for them to use. Ensure that the children understand that each question refers to the original time shown on the clock.

Name ______________________ Date __________

What time will it be?

Word bank

o'clock half past
one two three four
five six seven eight
nine ten eleven
twelve

What time does the clock show? [ ]

What time will it be one hour later? [ ]

What time will it be two hours later? [ ]

What time will it be three hours later? [ ]

Teacher's notes

Suggested objective: ***Solve problems about half past.***

Problems: Children to answer the questions above. They will need to interpret the questions, understanding the vocabulary of time. It would be a good idea to have a geared clock for them to use. Ensure that the children understand that each question refers to the original time shown on the clock.

Name ________________________ Date ____________

What time will it be?

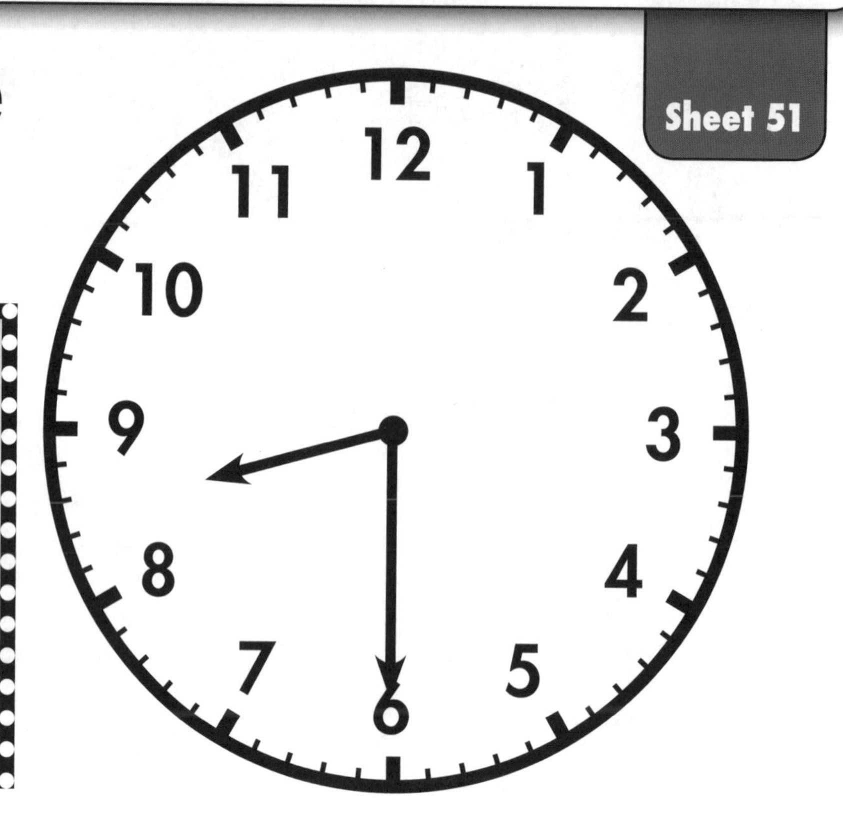

Word bank

o'clock half past
one two three four
five six seven eight
nine ten eleven
twelve

What time does the clock show? [ ]

What time will it be half an hour later? [ ]

What time will it be two hours later? [ ]

What time will it be three hours later? [ ]

Teacher's notes

Suggested objective: ***Solve problems about half past.***

Problems: Children answer the questions above. They will need to interpret the questions, understanding the vocabulary of time. It would be a good idea to have a geared clock for them to use. Ensure that the children understand that each question refers to the original time shown on the clock.

Name ______________________ Date ____________

How many pieces of pizza?

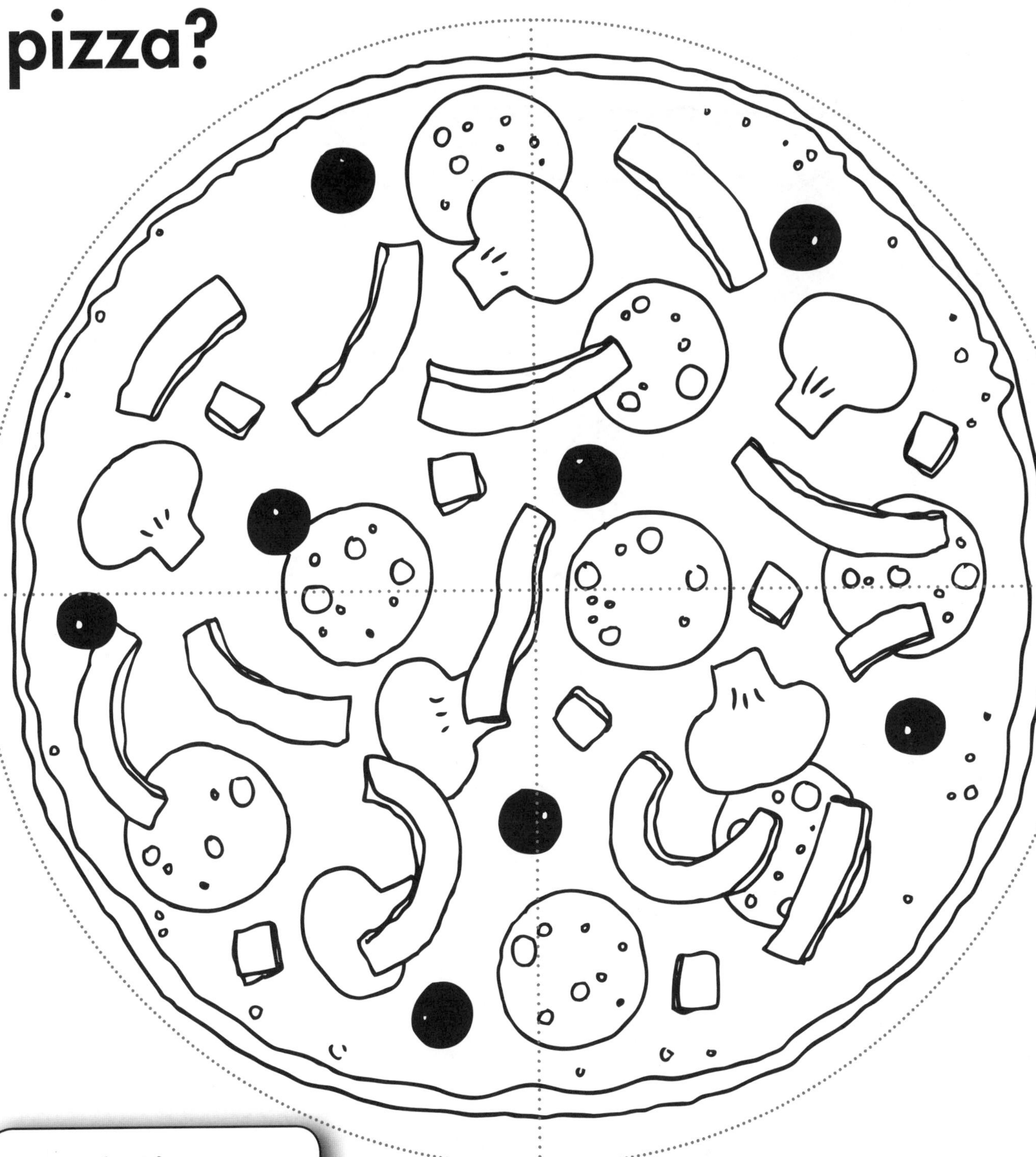

Teacher's notes

Suggested objective: ***Use the vocabulary of halves and quarters in context.***

Problems: ***How many whole pizzas are there? How many half pizzas are there? How many quarter pizzas are there? How many half pizzas make the same amount as a whole pizza? How many quarter pizzas make the same amount as a whole pizza? Show me three quarters of a pizza.***

Photocopy or print out three copies of the sheet, then laminate them for repeated use. Cut out one of the pizzas then cut the pizza exactly in half. Cut out another pizza, then cut it exactly in quarters.

Name ______________________ Date ____________

How many pieces of cake?

Sheet 53

Teacher's notes

Suggested objective: ***Use the vocabulary of halves and quarters in context.***

Problems: ***How many whole cakes are there? How many half cakes are there? How many quarter cakes are there? How many half cakes make the same amount as a whole cake? How many quarter cakes make the same amount as a whole cake? Show me three quarters of a cake.***
Photocopy or print out three copies of the sheet, then laminate them for repeated use. Cut out one of the cakes then cut the cake exactly in half. Cut out another cake, then cut it exactly in quarters.

Name ______________________ Date __________

Sheet 54

Which is the most popular fruit?

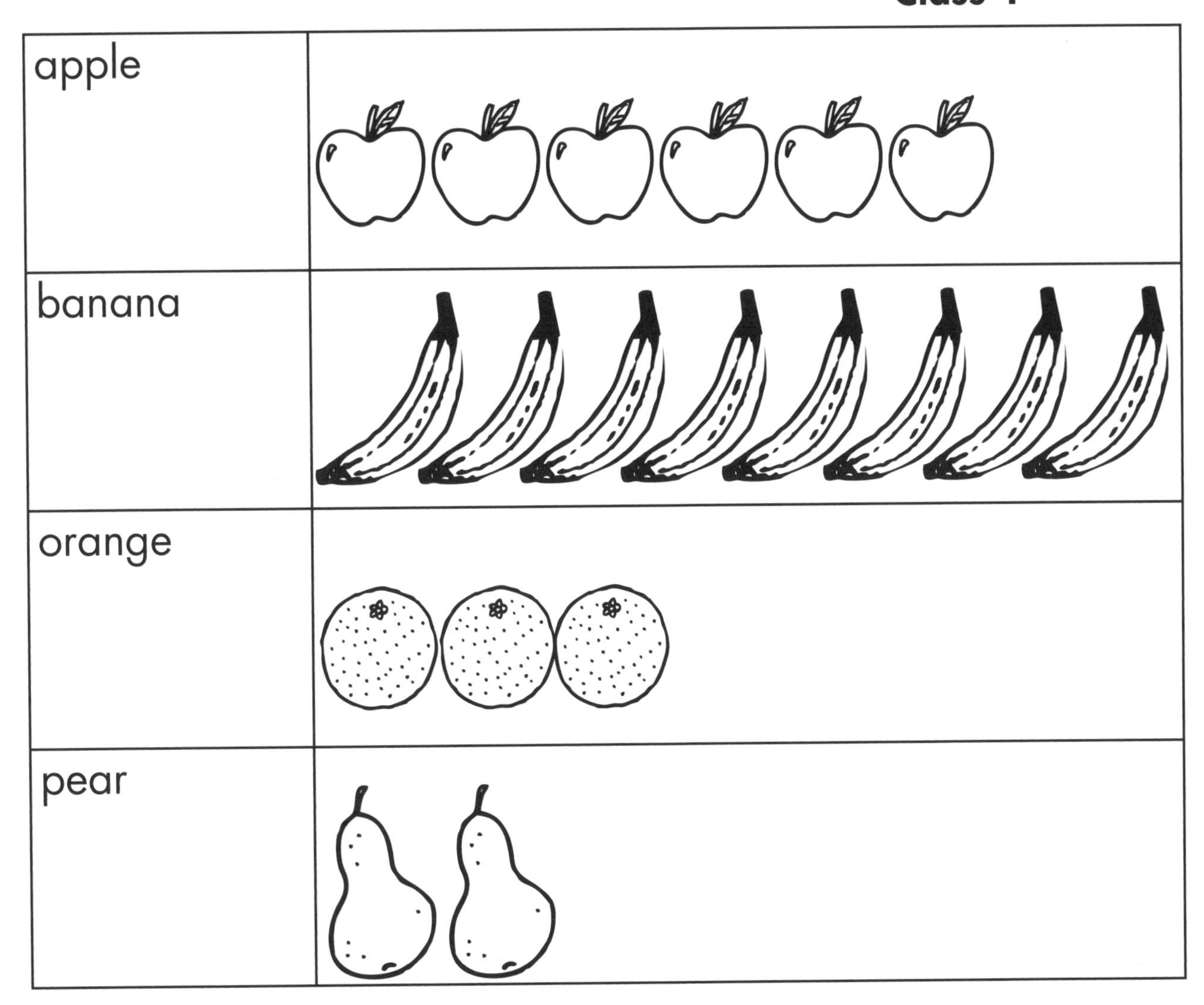

Teacher's notes

Suggested objective: *Interpret a simple pictogram.*

Problems: *What is the most popular fruit in Class 1? What is the least popular fruit? How many more children prefer bananas than apples? How many children are there altogether in Class 1?*

Name ______________________ Date __________

Which is the most popular fruit?

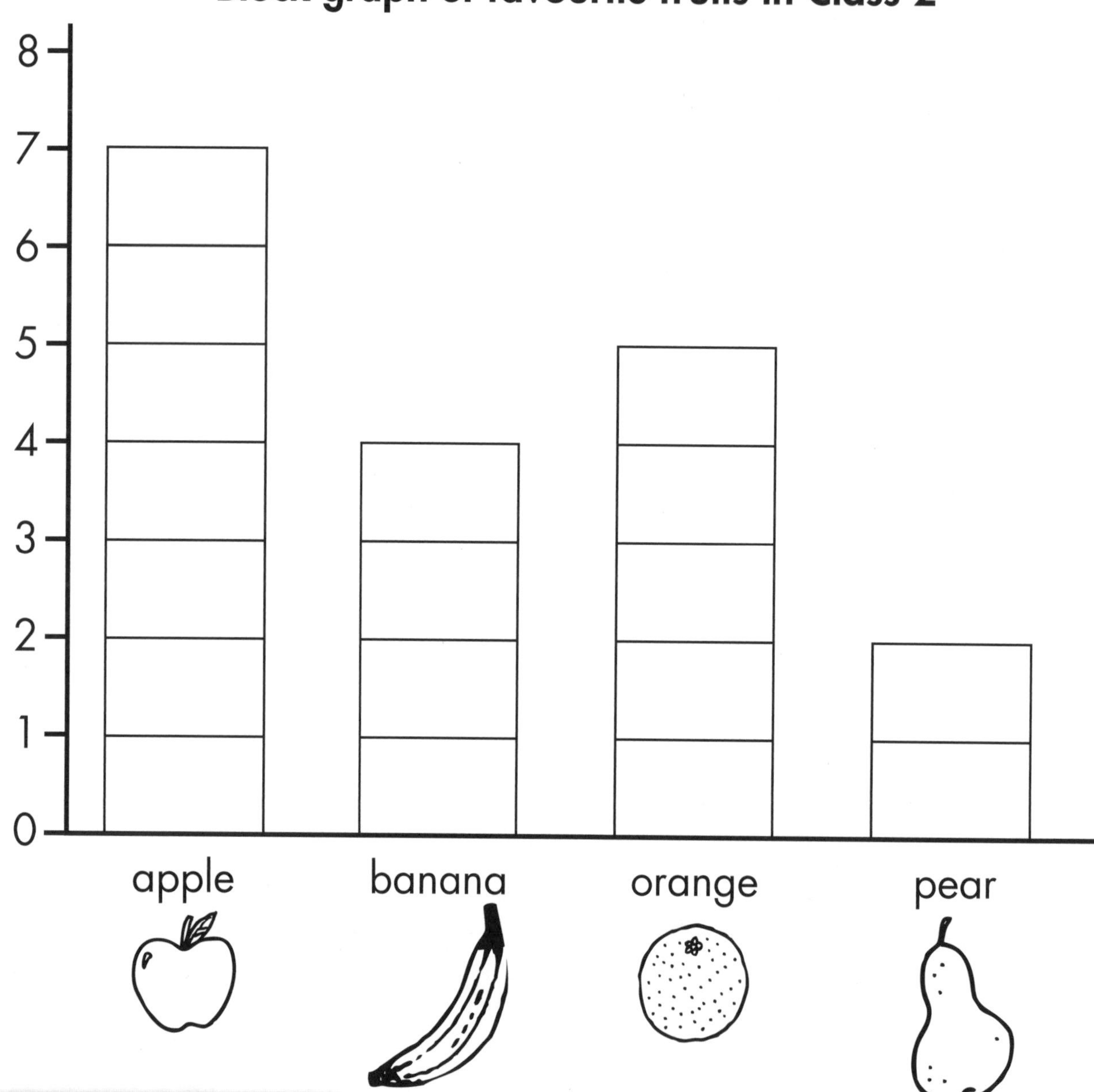

Teacher's notes

Suggested objective: ***Interpret a simple block graph.***

Problems: ***Which is the most popular fruit in Class 2? Which is the least popular fruit? How many more children prefer apples to bananas? How many children are there altogether in Class 2?***
Discuss the final question with the children - how can they find the answer to this?

Name ______________________ Date ____________

Which is the most popular fruit?

Sheet 56

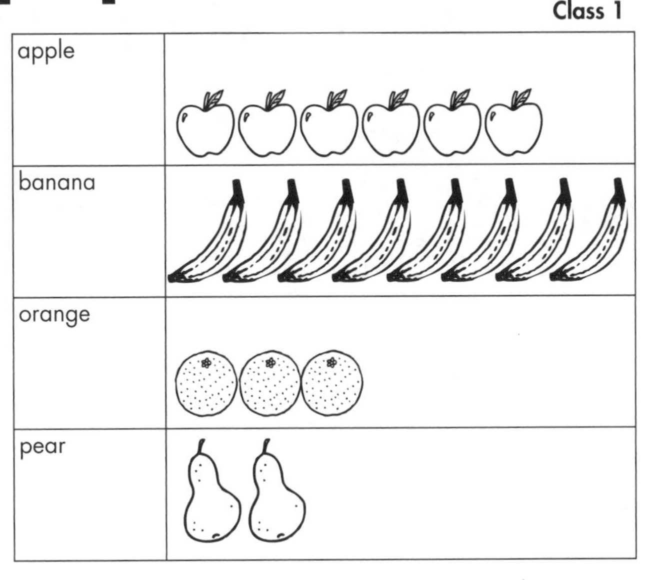

Class 2

8
7
6
5
4
3
2
1
0

apple banana orange pear

Which is the favourite fruit in Class 1?

Which is the most popular fruit in Class 2?

Which is the least popular fruit in Class 1?

Which is the least popular fruit in Class 2?

Which is your favourite fruit?

Teacher's notes

Suggested objective: ***Interpret a simple pictogram.***

Problems: Children answer the questions above. They will need to interpret the questions, understanding the vocabulary of data handling: favourite, most popular, least popular.

Name ______________________ Date ____________

Sheet 57

How can we count the squares?

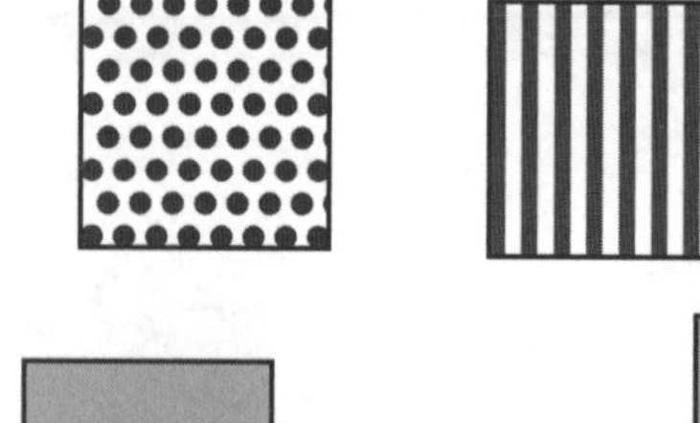

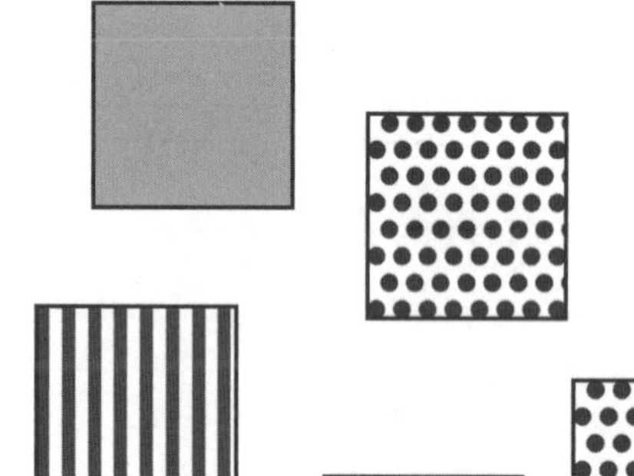

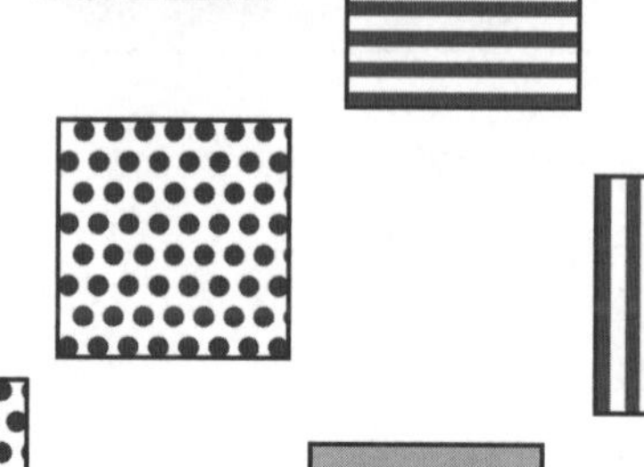

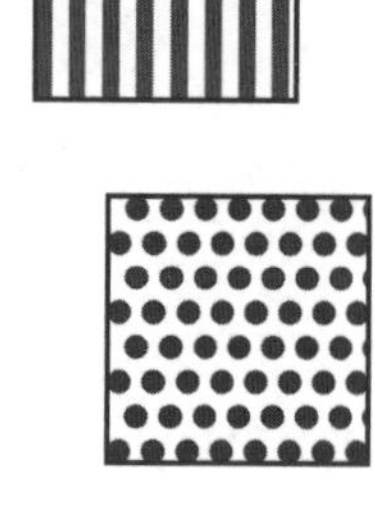

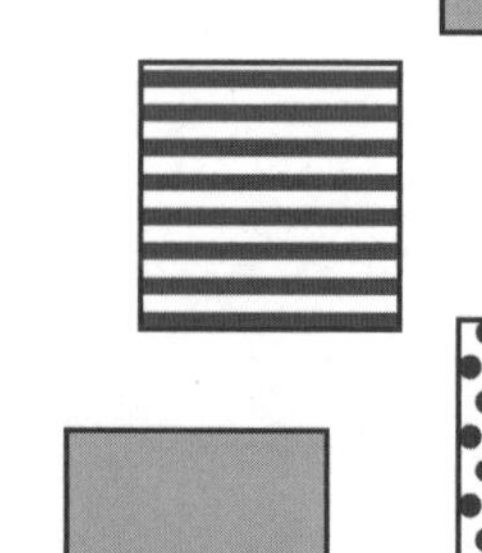

Teacher's notes

Suggested objective: ***Count reliably, possibly by grouping in tens, fives or twos.***

Problem: ***How can we count the squares? We don't want to miss any out. We only want to count each one once.***

Encourage the children to say how many squares they think there are – you could write down their estimates and explain that it doesn't matter if they haven't found exactly the right number. Allow the children to make suggestions, helping them to realise that there may be several ways of counting the squares.

Encourage the idea of counting in groups of ten, five or two. What's important is that they should be able to suggest a strategy. Once they have done so, see if they can follow it through successfully.

Name ______________________ Date ____________

How can we count the triangles?

Teacher's notes

Suggested objective: ***Count reliably, possibly by grouping in tens, fives or twos.***

Problem: ***How can we count the triangles? We don't want to miss any out. We only want to count each one once.***
Encourage the children to say how many triangles they think there are – you could write down their estimates and explain that it doesn't matter if they haven't found exactly the right number. Allow the children to make suggestions, helping them to realise that there may be several ways of counting the triangles.

Name ______________________ Date ______________

Sheet 59

How can we count the circles?

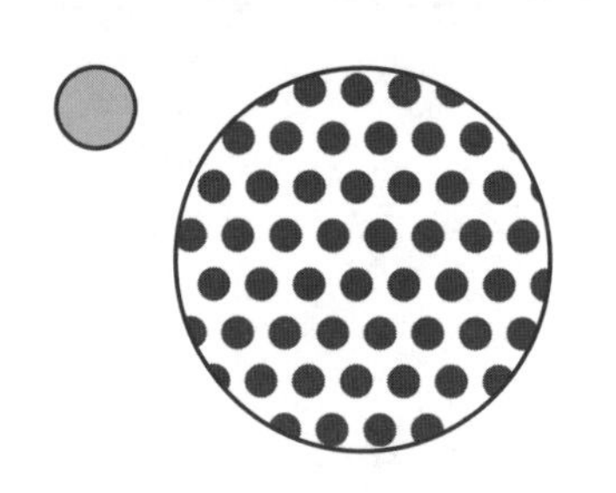

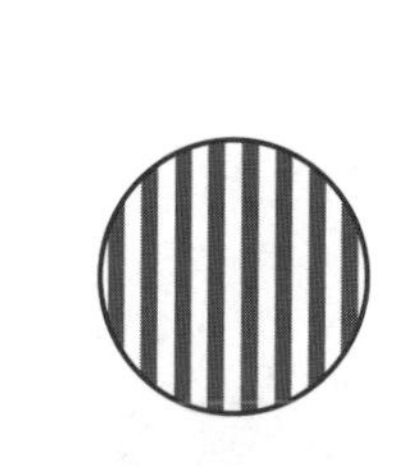
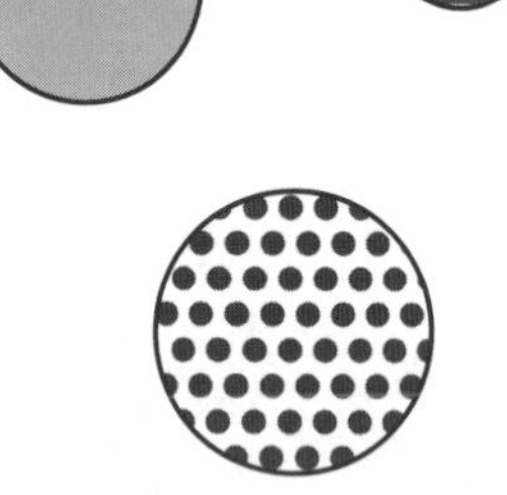

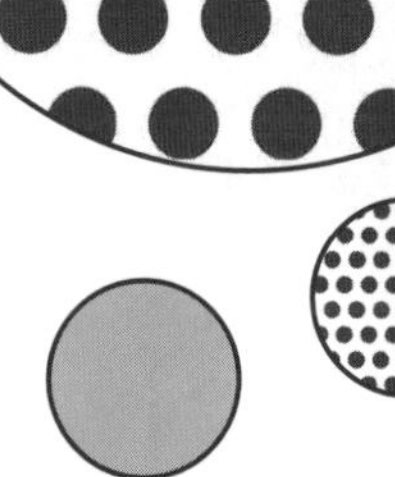

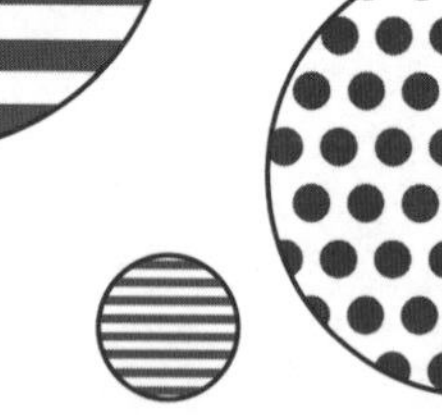
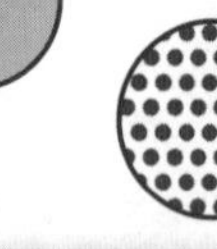
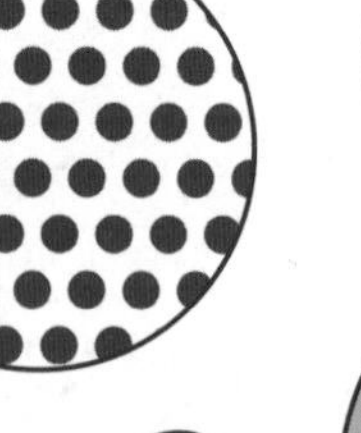

Teacher's notes

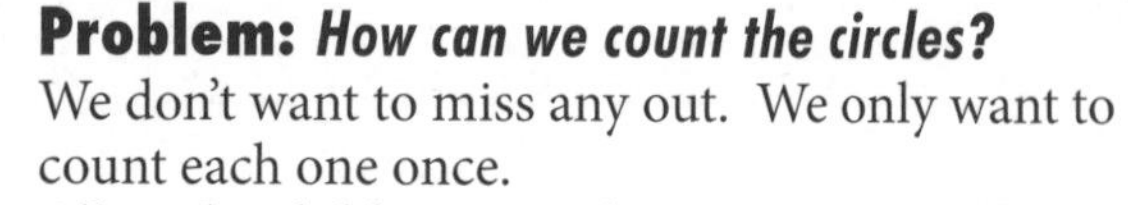

Suggested objective: ***Count reliably, possibly by grouping in tens, fives or twos.***

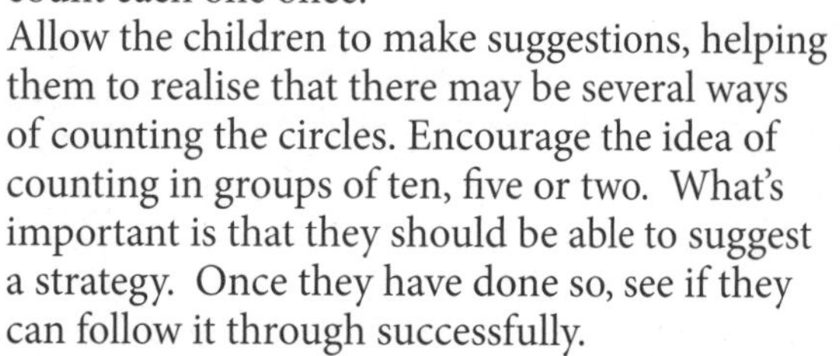

Problem: ***How can we count the circles?***
We don't want to miss any out. We only want to count each one once.
Allow the children to make suggestions, helping them to realise that there may be several ways of counting the circles. Encourage the idea of counting in groups of ten, five or two. What's important is that they should be able to suggest a strategy. Once they have done so, see if they can follow it through successfully.

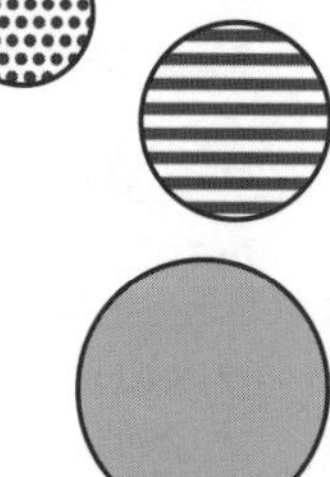

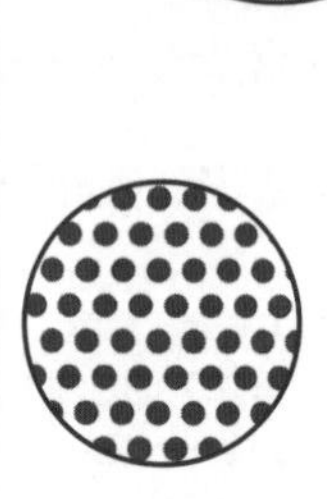
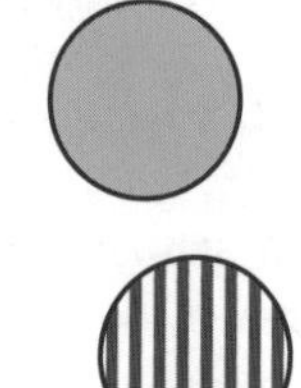

Name ______________________ *Date* __________

How can we count the pentagons?

Teacher's notes

Suggested objective: ***Count reliably, possibly by grouping in tens, fives or twos.***

Problem: ***How can we count the pentagons?***
We don't want to miss any out. We only want to count each one once.
Allow the children to make suggestions, helping them to realise that there may be several ways of counting the pentagons. Encourage the idea of counting in groups of ten, five or two. What's important is that they should be able to suggest a strategy. Once they have done so, see if they can follow it through successfully.

Name ______________________ Date ____________

How many sticks do we need?

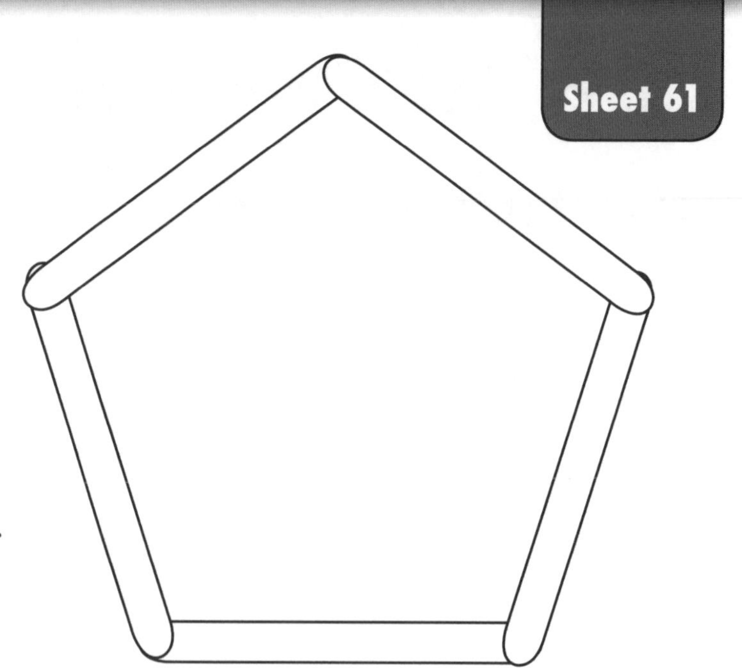

This pentagon has been made using lollipop sticks.

We would need ten sticks to make two separate pentagons.

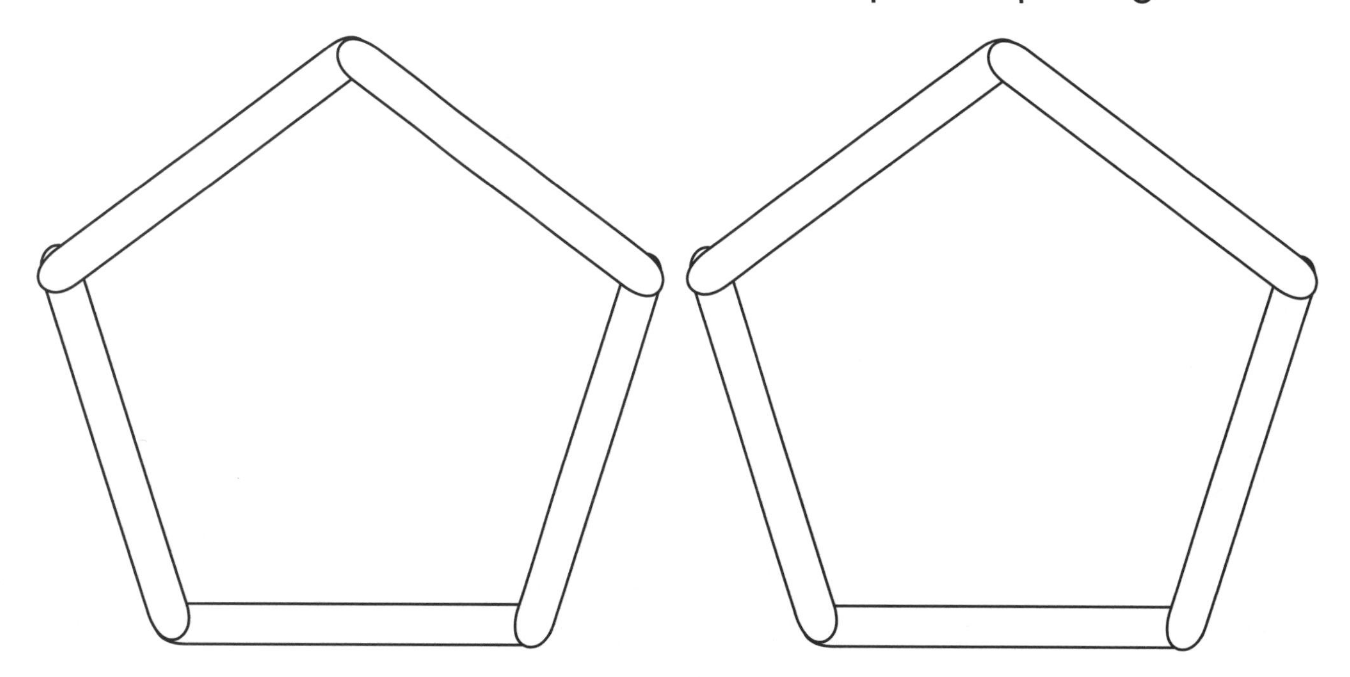

Teacher's notes

Suggested objective: ***Identify the properties of pentagons.***

Problem: ***How many lollipop sticks do we need to make three separate pentagons? How many sticks would we need to make four pentagons like these?***
Look at the pentagons and how they are made. You could provide the children with lollipop sticks to make their own pentagons.

Name ______________________ Date ____________

How many sticks do we need?

Sheet 62

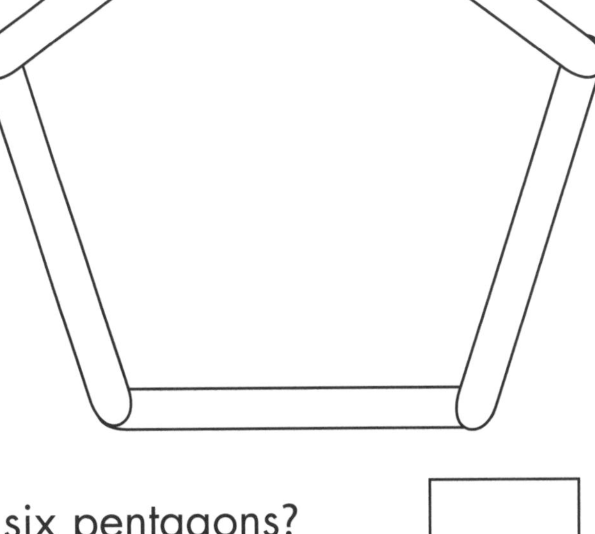

How many sticks are needed to make....

one pentagon?

two pentagons? 

three pentagons? 

four pentagons? 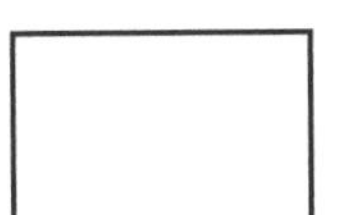

five pentagons?

six pentagons?

seven pentagons? 

eight pentagons? 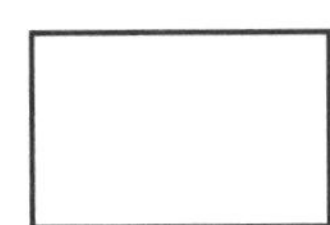

nine pentagons? 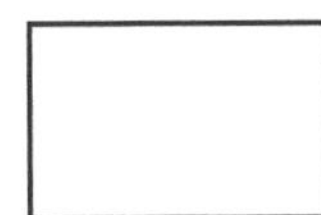

ten pentagons? 

Teacher's notes

Suggested objective: ***Use pentagons to help derive multiplication facts for the 5 times table.***

Problems: Support the children in answering the questions, thus building up the five times table. You could provide lollipop sticks for them to make their own pentagons.

Name ______________________ Date ____________

What shapes are these?

Sheet 63

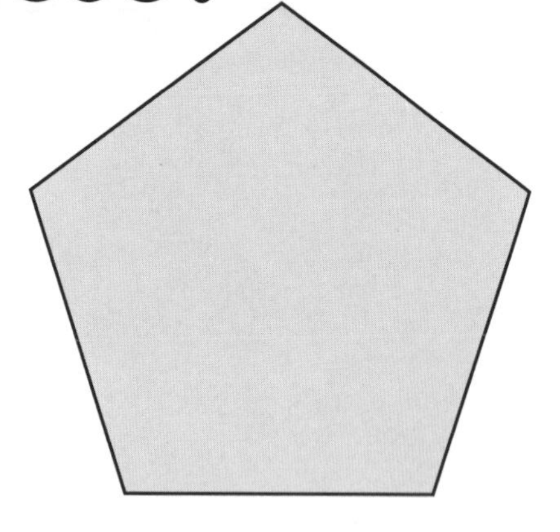

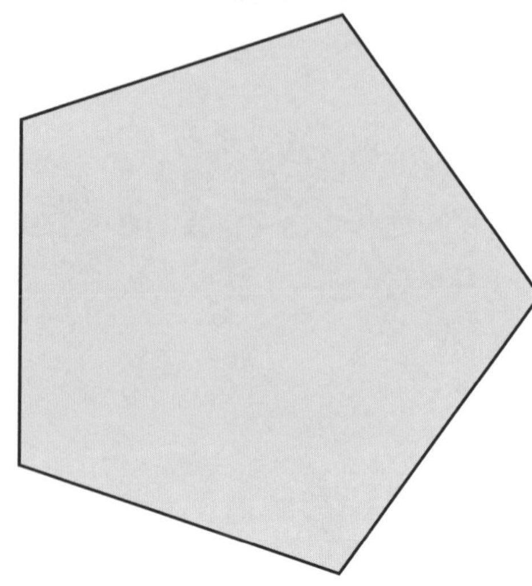

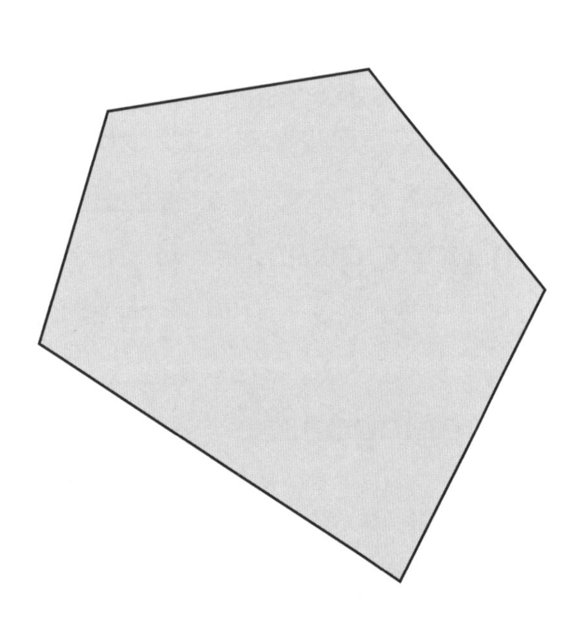

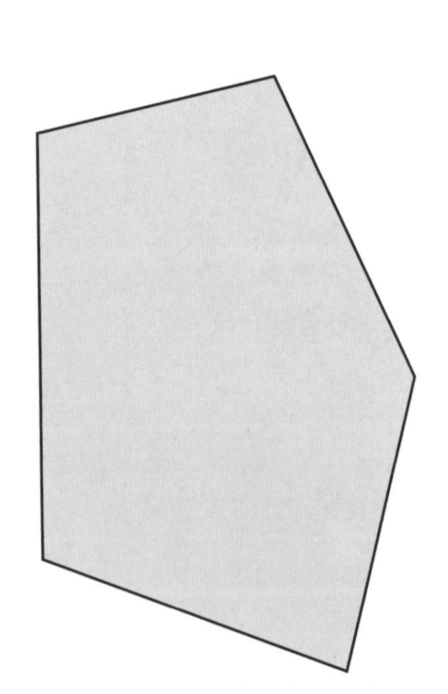

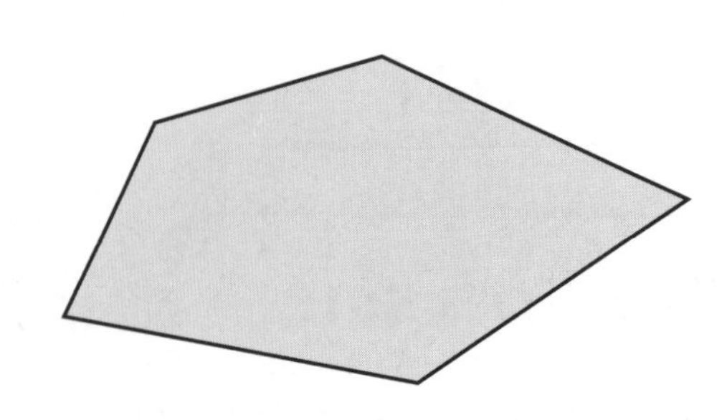

Teacher's notes

This sheet to be used in conjunction with Sheet 66.
Suggested objective: ***Identify the properties of pentagons.***

Problem: ***What shapes are these?***
Photocopy or print out two copies of the sheet and laminate both. Cut out the shapes from one of the sheets. The children should be able to refer to the properties of the shapes to identify them all correctly as pentagons. They are not expected to know the terms 'regular' and 'irregular' but they should be able to see that two of the pentagons have equal sides and equal angles.

Name ______________________ Date ______________

What shapes are these?

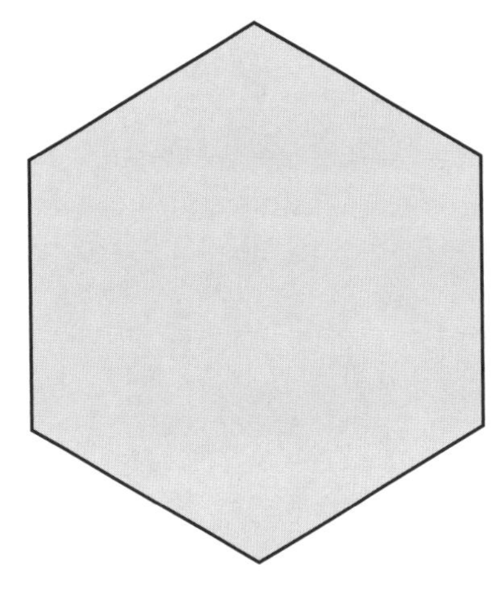

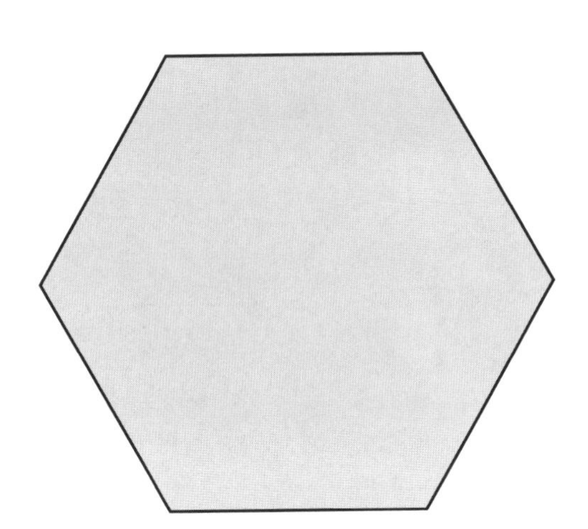

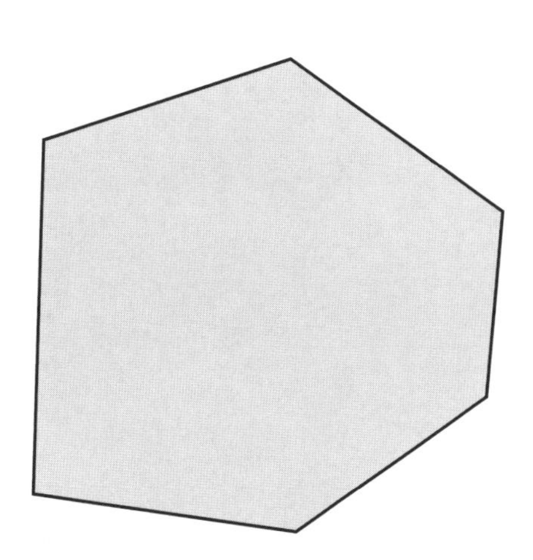

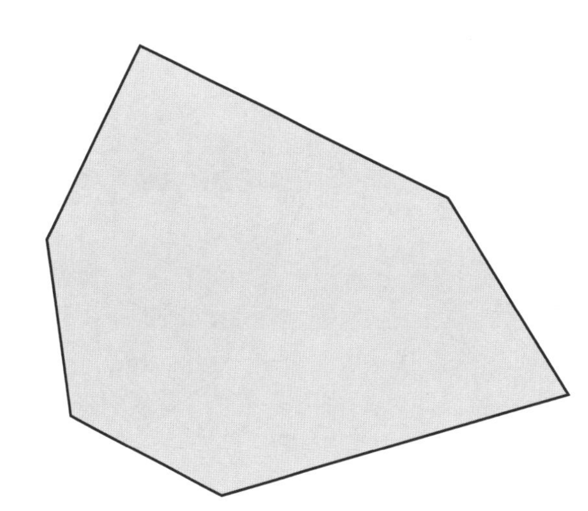

Teacher's notes

This sheet to be used in conjunction with Sheet 66.
Suggested objective: ***Identify the properties of hexagons.***

Problem: ***What shapes are these?***
Photocopy or print out two copies of the sheet and laminate both. Cut out the shapes from one of the sheets. The children should be able to refer to the properties of the shapes to identify them all correctly as hexagons. They are not expected to know the terms 'regular' and 'irregular' but they should be able to see that two of the hexagons have equal sides and equal angles.

Name ____________________ Date __________

Sheet 65

What shapes are these?

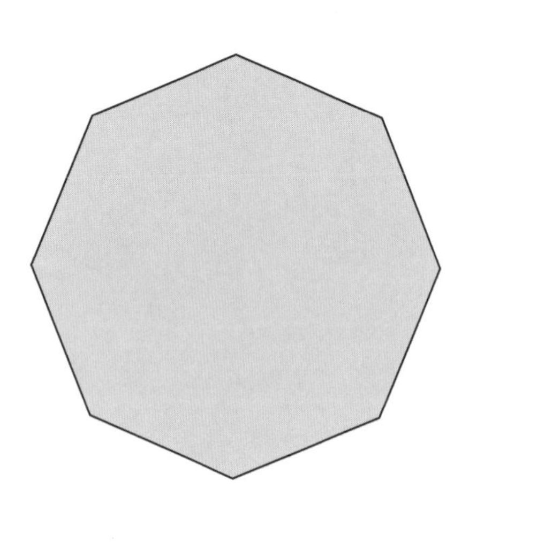

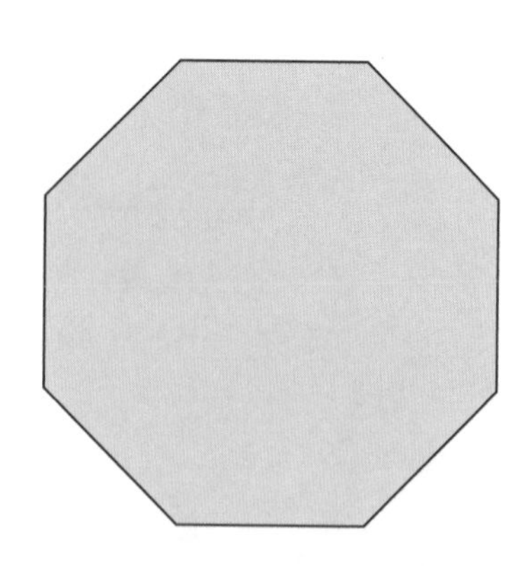

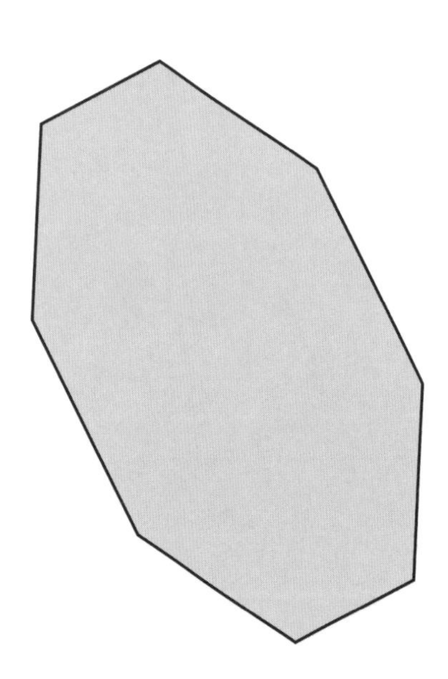

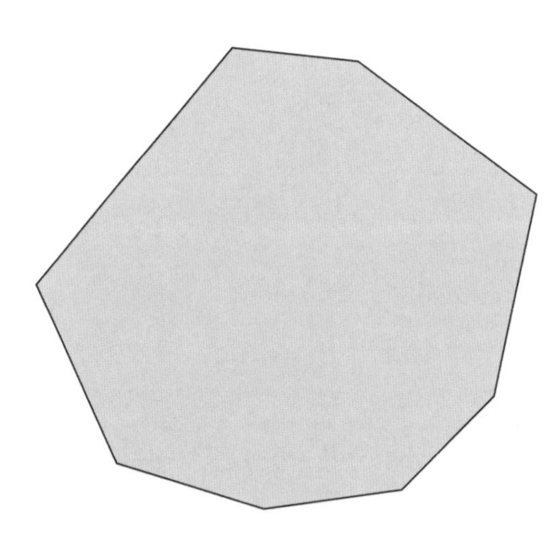

Teacher's notes

This activity sheet to be used in conjunction with Sheet 66.
Suggested objective: ***Identify the properties of octagons.***

Problem: ***What shapes are these?***
Photocopy or print out two copies of the sheet and laminate both. Cut out the shapes from one of the sheets. The children should be able to refer to the properties of the shapes to identify them all correctly as octagons. They are not expected to know the terms 'regular' and 'irregular' but they should be able to see that two of the octagons have equal sides and equal angles.

Name ______________________ Date ____________

Can you sort the shapes?

Sheet 66

pentagons	not pentagons

Teacher's notes

Use the cut out shapes from activity sheets 63, 64 and 65.

Suggested objective: ***Sort shapes into a table.***

Problem: ***Can you sort the shapes?***
The children should be able to refer to the properties of the shapes to identify which ones are pentagons to place in the left-hand column; the others then go in the 'not pentagons' column.
Extension problem: Provide two further tables for sorting the shapes into 'hexagons' and 'not hexagons', and 'octagons' and 'not octagons'.

Name ____________________ Date ____________

Can you sort the shapes?

Sheet 67

equal sides	not equal sides

Teacher's notes

Use the cut out shapes from activity sheets 63, 64 and 65.

Suggested objective: ***Sort shapes into a table.***

Problem: ***Can you sort the shapes?***

This is a much harder activity than on Sheet 66 as here the children will find two pentagons, two hexagons and two octagons to go in the lefthand column, with the remaining shapes going in the righthand column.

Name ______________________ Date __________

How much shall I spend?

Sheet 68

These sweets cost 10p each.

sweet necklace
10p

chewy bottle 10p

lollipop 10p

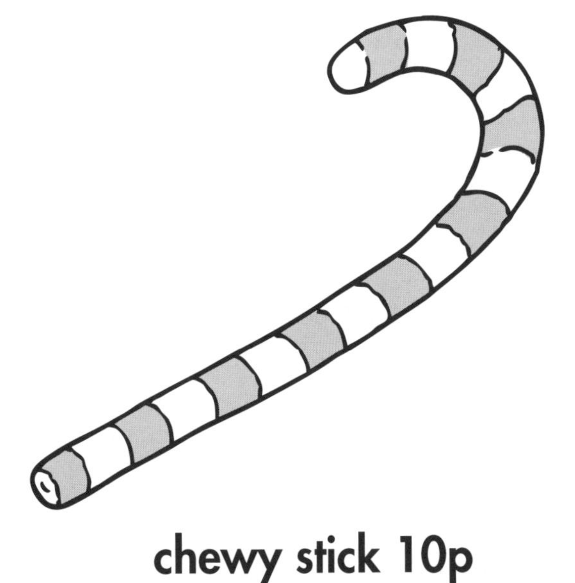

chewy stick 10p

Teacher's notes

Suggested objective: ***Use mental calculation strategies to solve number problems involving money.***

Problems: Ask the children how much one of the sweets would cost, then ask how much two would cost, then three, then four. If you feel that the children are confident enough, ask them what change there would be from 50p or £1 for each combination of sweets.

Name ______________________ Date ____________

What change will I have?

Sheet 69

I buy one sweet necklace and one chewy bottle.
Total cost = ☐ Change from 50p = ☐

I buy one chewy stick, a lollipop and one chewy bottle.
Total cost = ☐ Change from 50p = ☐

I buy one chewy stick and one chewy bottle.
Total cost = ☐ Change from £1 = ☐

I buy three lollipops.
Total cost = ☐ Change from £1 = ☐

Teacher's notes

This activity sheet to be used in conjunction with Sheet 68.
Suggested objective: ***Use mental calculation strategies to solve number problems involving money.***

Problems: Children answer the questions above. In observing them dealing with the questions you are able to assess several aspects of the Assessment Focuses for Using and Applying Mathematics at Level 2: Do the children select the mathematics they use in some classroom activities, eg with support? Do they find a starting point, identifying key facts/relevant information? Do they use apparatus, diagrams, role-play, etc. to represent and clarify a problem? Do they adopt a suggested model or systematic approach? Do they use mathematical content from levels 1 and 2 to solve problems and investigate?

Name ______________________ Date __________

How much shall I spend?

Sheet 70

These sweets cost 5p each.

chocolate saw 5p

chewy cherry 5p

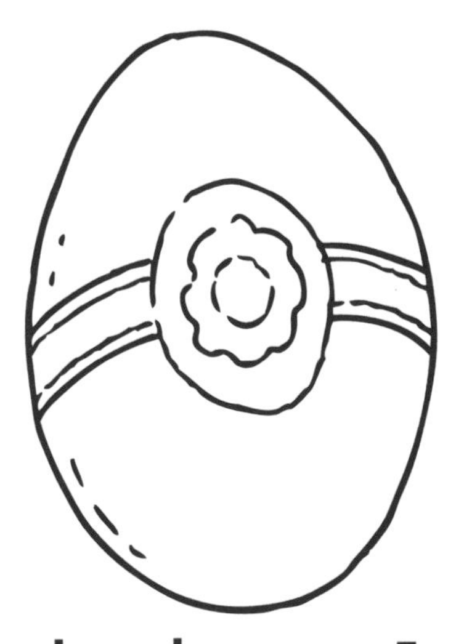

chocolate egg 5p

sugar mouse 5p

Teacher's notes

Suggested objective: ***Use mental calculation strategies to solve number problems involving money.***

Problems: Ask the children how much one of the sweets would cost, then ask how much two would cost, then three, then four. If you feel that the children are confident enough, ask them what change there would be from 20p, 50p or £1.

Name ______________________ Date ______________

Buying sweets at the shop

Sheet 71

chocolate saw 5p

chocolate egg 5p

chewy cherry 5p

sugar mouse 5p

I buy one sugar mouse and one chewy cherry.

Total cost = [ ] Change from 20p = [ ]

I buy one chocolate saw, one chocolate egg and one sugar mouse.

Total cost = [ ] Change from 20p = [ ]

I buy one each of all four sweets.

Total cost = [ ] Change from 20p = [ ]

I buy two chocolate eggs and one sugar mouse.

Total cost = [ ] Change from 50p = [ ]

Teacher's notes

This activity sheet to be used in conjunction with Sheet 70.

Suggested objective: ***Use mental calculation strategies to solve number problems involving money.***

Problems: Children answer the questions above. In observing them dealing with the questions you are able to assess several aspects of the Assessment Focuses for Using and Applying Mathematics at Level 2: Do the children select the mathematics they use in some classroom activities, eg with support? Do they find a starting point, identifying key facts/relevant information? Do they use apparatus, diagrams, role-play, etc. to represent and clarify a problem? Do they adopt a suggested model or systematic approach? Do they use mathematical content from levels 1 and 2 to solve problems and investigate?

Name ______________________ Date ____________

Buying sweets at the shop

Sheet 72

chocolate saw 5p

chocolate egg 5p

chewy cherry 5p

sugar mouse 5p

sweet necklace 10p

chewy bottle 10p

lollipop 10p

chewy stick 10p

I buy one chewy bottle, one lollipop and one sugar mouse.

Total cost = ☐ Change from 50p = ☐

I buy one each of all the chewy sweets.

Total cost = ☐ Change from £1 = ☐

I buy two lollipops and two chocolate eggs.

Total cost = ☐ Change from 50p = ☐

I buy seven necklaces.

Total cost = ☐ Change from £1 = ☐

Teacher's notes

This activity sheet to be used in conjuction with Sheets 68 and 70.

Suggested objective: ***Use mental calculation strategies to solve number problems involving money.***

Problems: Children answer the questions above. In observing them dealing with the questions you are able to assess several aspects of the Assessment Focuses for Using and Applying Mathematics at Level 2: Do the children select the mathematics they use in some classroom activities, eg with support? Do they find a starting point, identifying key facts/relevant information? Do they use apparatus, diagrams, role-play, etc. to represent and clarify a problem? Do they adopt a suggested model or systematic approach? Do they use mathematical content from levels 1 and 2 to solve problems and investigate?

Name ______________________________ Date ______________

Kim's money

Sheet 73

Teacher's notes

This activity sheet to be used in conjunction with Sheet 68.

Suggested objective: ***Use mental calculation strategies to solve number problems involving money.***

Problems: ***How much money does Kim have?***

Can Kim afford to buy a sweet necklace and a lollipop? How much more money does Kim need to have 20p?

Name ______________________ Date ____________

Hala's money

Sheet 74

Teacher's notes

This activity sheet to be used in conjunction with Sheet 68.

Suggested objective: ***Use mental calculation strategies to solve number problems involving money.***

Problems: How much money does Hala have?

Can Hala afford to buy a sweet necklace? How much more money does Hala need to have 20p?

Name ______________________ *Date* __________

Ben's money

Sheet 75

Teacher's notes

This activity sheet to be used in conjunction with Sheets 68 and 70.
Suggested objective: ***Use mental calculation strategies to solve number problems involving money.***

Problems: ***How much money does Ben have?***
Can Ben afford to buy a chewy bottle and a chocolate egg? How much more money does Ben need to have 20p?

Name ______________________ Date ____________

Ali's money

Sheet 76

Teacher's notes

This activity sheet to be used in conjunction with with Sheets 68 and 70. (Print and laminate Sheets 73, 74, 75 and 76 also to make comparisons with other children).

Suggested objective: ***Use mental calculation strategies to solve number problems involving money.***

Problems: ***How much money does Ali have?***
Can Ali afford to buy 3 sugar mice and a chewy cherry? How much more than 20p has Ali got? How much more than each of the other children has Ali got?

Extension Problem: Make comparisons between the amounts of money each child has. Who has the most? Who has the least? Who has more than 10p? Who has less than 10p? How much have the four children got altogether?

Name ______________________ Date ____________

How much money?

Sheet 77

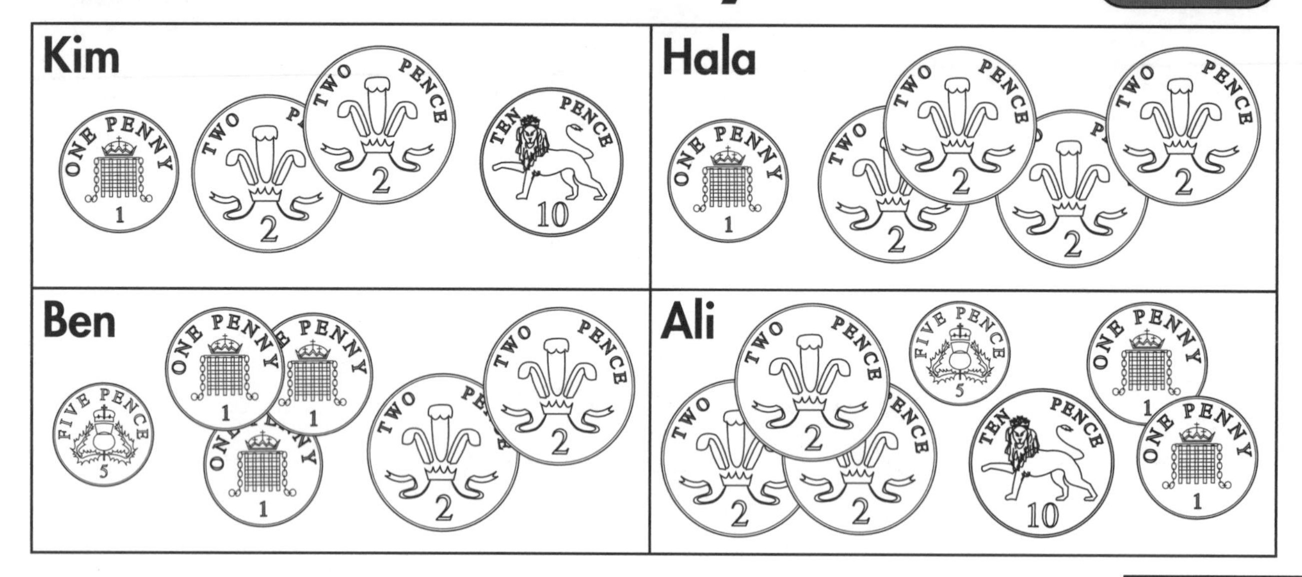

How much money has Kim got? ☐

How much money has Hala got? ☐

How much money has Ben got? ☐

How much money has Ali got? ☐

How much more money would Ali need to have 50p? ☐

If Kim had double her amount of money, how much would she have? ☐

If Ben spends half his money, how much would he have left? ☐

Teacher's notes

Suggested ***objective: Use mental calculation strategies to solve number problems involving money.***

Problems: Children answer the questions above. In observing them dealing with the questions you are able to assess several aspects of the Assessment Focuses for Using and Applying Mathematics and for Number: Do they find a starting point, identifying key facts/relevant information? Do the children use the knowledge that subtraction is the inverse of addition, eg are they beginning to understand subtraction as 'difference'? Can they make related number sentences involving addition and subtraction? Do they understand halving as a way of 'undoing' doubling and vice versa?

Name ______________________ Date ____________

Sheet 78

How many ways can you make 5p?

5p	
5p	
5p	
5p	

Teacher's notes

Suggested objective: ***Devise a strategy for finding all ways of making a total of 5p.***

Problem: ***How many ways can you make 5p?***
Ask individual children to make 5p, using different coins. There are only four ways of making 5p: one 5p coin; two 2p coins with one 1p coin; one 2p coin with three 1p coins; five 1p coins.
For some children this is a very difficult concept, not helped by the sizes of the various coins! You could real coins.

Name ________________________ Date ____________

How many ways can you make 10p?

Sheet 79

10p	
10p	
10p	
10p	
10p	
10p	
10p	
10p	
10p	
10p	
10p	

Teacher's notes

Suggested objective: ***Devise a strategy for finding all ways of making a total of 10p.***

Problem: ***How many ways can you make 10p?***
Ask individual children to make 10p, using different coins. There are eleven different ways of making 10p: one 10p coin; two 5p coins; one 5p, two 2p coins, one 1p; one 5p, one 2p, three 1p coins; one 5p, five 1p coins; five 2p coins; ten 1p coins; four 2p coins, two 1p coins; three 2p coins, four 1p coins; two 2p coins, six 1p coins; one 2p, eight 1p coins. For some children this is a very difficult concept.

Name ______________________ Date ____________

Sheet 80

How much more money does each child need to make 20p?

1p 2p 5p 10p 20p

Kim

Hala

Ben

Ali

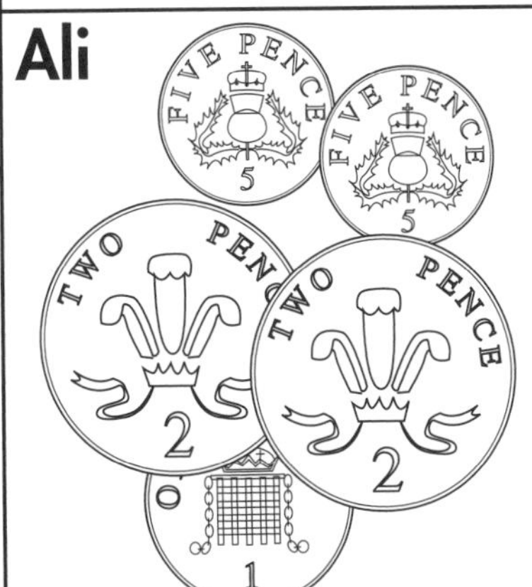

Teacher's notes

Suggested objective: ***Use mental calculation strategies to solve number problems involving money.***

Problems: ***How much more money does each child need to make 20p?***
Which two children have the same amount of money? Who has the least amount? Who has the most? How much more money does Ben have than Kim? How much more does Ali have than Hala? How much do the two girls have altogether? How much do the two boys have altogether? How much do the four children have altogether? You could use real coins to work out the answers to the questions posed on this sheet.

Name ______________________ Date ______________

Sheet 81

How much more money does each child need to make 50p?

1p 2p 5p 10p 20p 50p

Kim

Hala

Ben

Ali

Teacher's notes

Suggested objective: ***Use mental calculation strategies to solve number problems involving money.***

Problems: ***How much more money does each child need to make 50p?***
Who has the least amount? Who has the most? How much more money does Ali have than Ben? How much more does Ali have than Hala? How much do the two girls have altogether? How much do the two boys have altogether? How much do the four children have altogether? You could use real coins to work out the answers to the questions posed on this sheet.

Name ______________________ Date ____________

How much money is there in each set?

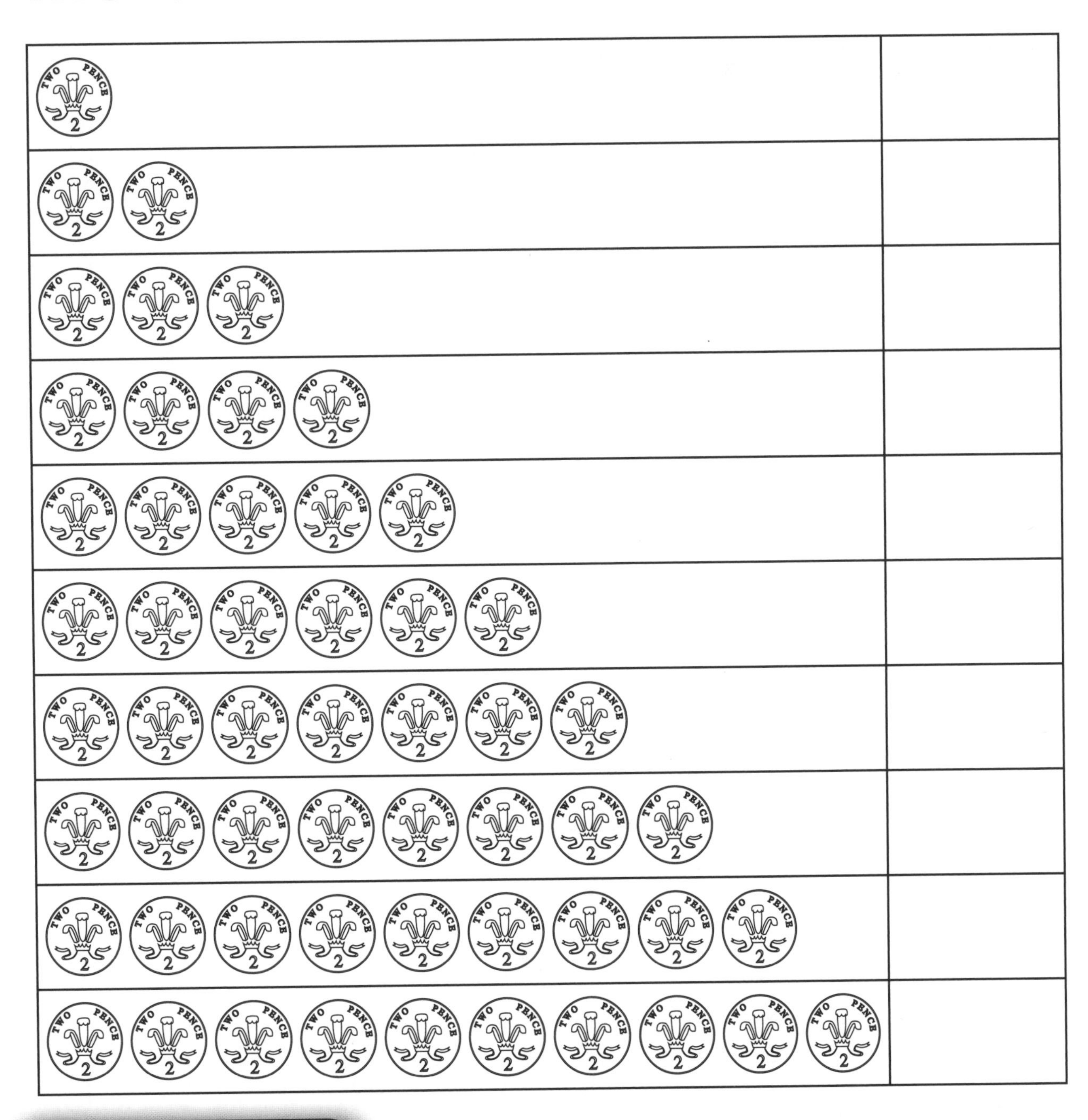

Teacher's notes

Suggested objective: ***Find the facts for the 2 times table using 2p coins.***

Problem: ***How much money is there in each set?***
This sheet gives pupils the opportunity to derive the multiplication facts for the 2 times table, in the real world context of money.
You could use real coins to work out the answers to the questions.

Name ______________________ Date ____________

Sheet 83

How many 2p coins do you need to make each amount of money?

		Number of 2p coins
14p		
6p		
10p		
8p		
16p		
20p		
12p		
4p		
18p		

Teacher's notes

Suggested objective: ***Use 2p coins to find facts from the 2 times table.***

Problem: ***How many 2p coins do you need to make each amount of money?***
This sheet gives pupils the opportunity to solve simple practical problems that involve combining groups of 2. You may wish to extend the activity by asking the children which other coins they could use to make up each amount of money.
You could use real coins to work out the answers to the questions and place them in the second column.
Extension Problem: ***Using any type of coins, what is the least number of coins needed for each amount?***

Name ______________________ Date ____________

How much money is there in each set?

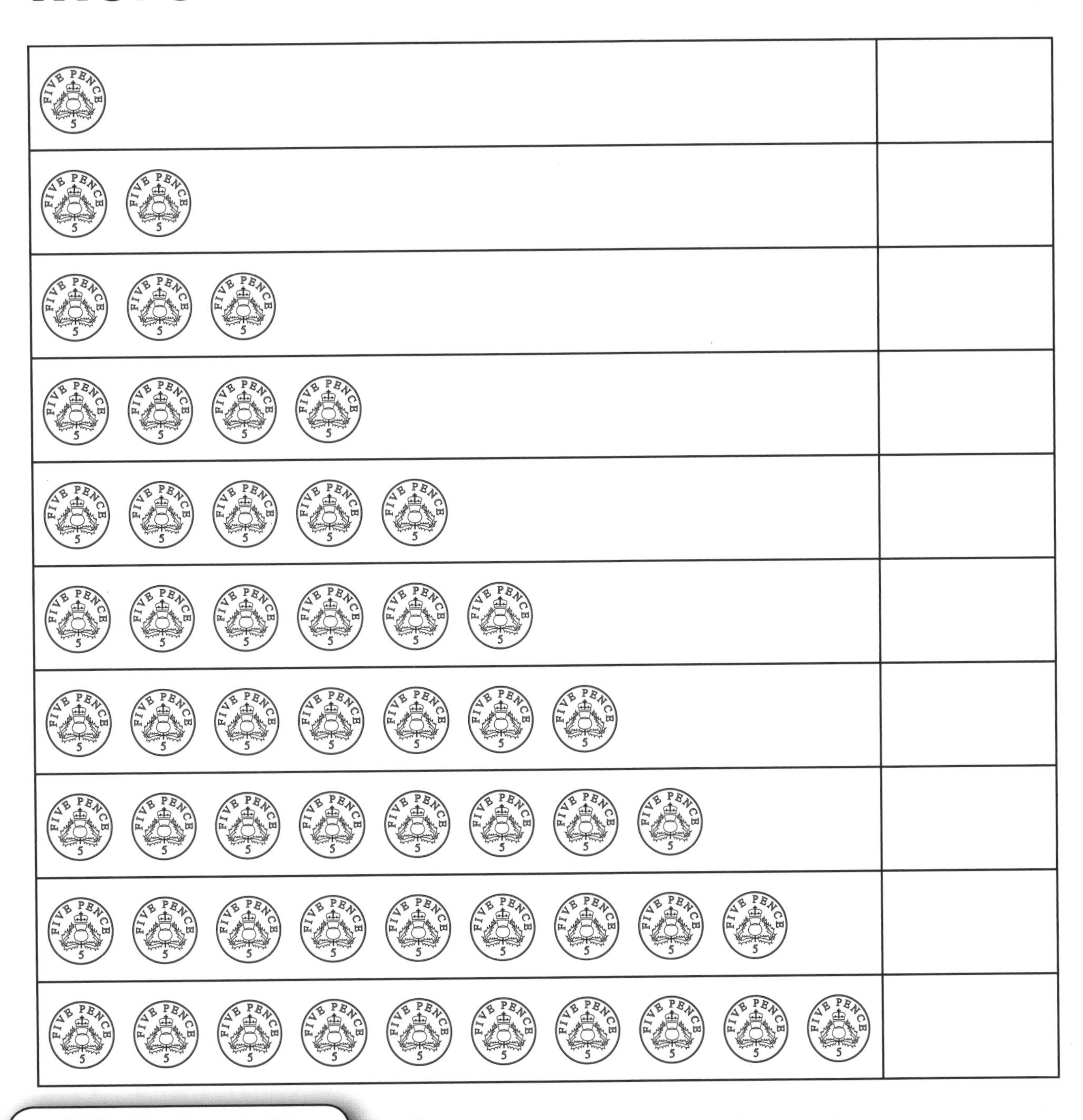

Teacher's notes

Suggested objective: ***Find the facts for the 5 times table using 5p coins.***

Problem: ***How much money is there in each set?***
This sheet gives pupils the opportunity to derive the multiplication facts for the 5 times table, in the real world context of money. You could use real coins to work out the answers to the questions.

Name ______________________ *Date* ____________

Sheet 85

How many 5p coins do you need to make each amount of money?

		Number of 5p coins
15p		
30p		
10p		
35p		
20p		
25p		
40p		
50p		
45p		

Teacher's notes

Suggested objective: ***Use 5p coins to find facts from the 5 times table.***

Problem: ***How many 5p coins do you need to make each amount of money?***
This sheet gives pupils the opportunity to solve simple practical problems that involve combining groups of 5. You may wish to extend the activity by asking the children which other coins they could use to make up each amount of money.
Extension Problem: ***Using any type of coins, what is the least number of coins needed for each amount?***
You could use real coins to work out the answers to the questions.

Name ______________________ Date ____________

How many stamps?

Sheet 86

Jim collects stamps.
How many has he got?

Teacher's notes

This activity sheet to be used in conjunction with Sheets 87 and 88 so that comparisons can be made.
Suggested objective: ***Solve problems using addition, subtraction and multiplication.***

Problems: ***How many stamps does Jim have?***
How many more stamps does Jim need to have 20 stamps? Help the children to count the number of stamps that Jim has. Encourage them to count in twos, then to add on the extra single stamp.

Name ______________________ Date ____________

How many stamps?

Sheet 87

Barney collects stamps. How many has he got?

Teacher's notes

This activity sheet to be used in conjunction with Sheets 86 and 88 so that comparisons can be made.

Suggested objective: ***Solve problems using addition, subtraction and multiplication.***

Problems: ***How many stamps does Barney have?***

Help the children to count the number of stamps that Barney has. Encourage them to count in fives. How many more does Barney need to have 30? 50? 100?

Name ______________________________ Date ______________

How many stamps?

Sheet 88

Amina collects stamps. How many has she got?

Teacher's notes

This activity sheet to be used in conjunction with Sheets 86 and 87 so that comparisons can be made.
Suggested objective: ***Solve problems using addition, subtraction and multiplication.***

Problems: Help the children to count the number of stamps that Amina has. Encourage them to count in fives, then to add on the extra four stamps.
Extension Problem: ***Who has more than 20 stamps?***
Who has fewer than 20 stamps? How many have they got altogether? How many more than Jim has Barney got? How many fewer than Barney has Amina got?

Name ______________________ Date ____________

How many stamps?

Sheet 89

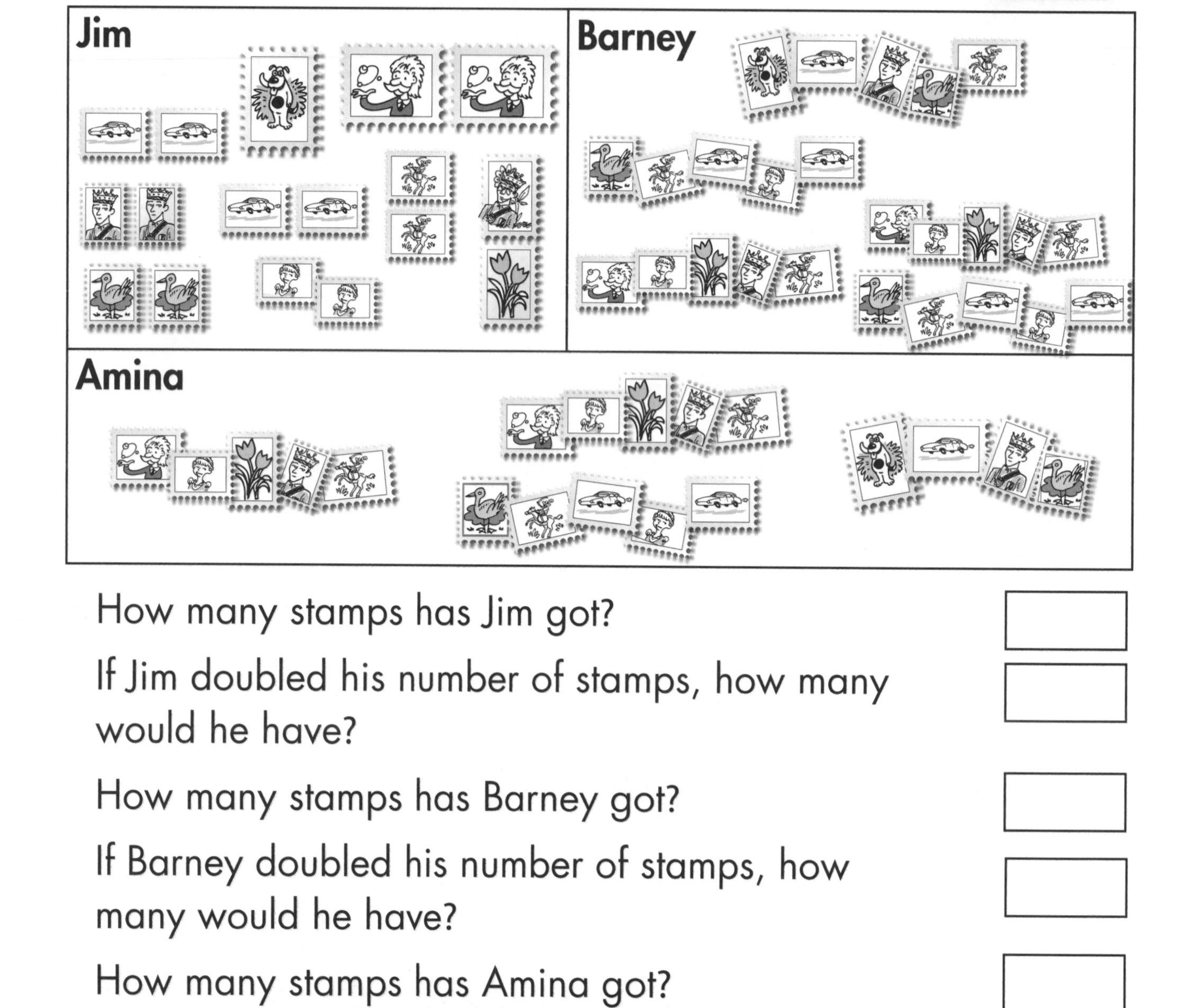

How many stamps has Jim got? [ ]

If Jim doubled his number of stamps, how many would he have? [ ]

How many stamps has Barney got? [ ]

If Barney doubled his number of stamps, how many would he have? [ ]

How many stamps has Amina got? [ ]

If Amina doubled her number of stamps, how many would she have? [ ]

Teacher's notes

Suggested objective: ***Solve problems using addition, subtraction and multiplication.***

Problems: Children answer the questions above. In observing them dealing with the questions you are able to assess several aspects of the Assessment Focuses for Using and Applying Mathematics and for Number: Do they find a starting point, identifying key facts/relevant information? Do they adopt a suggested model or systematic approach? Do they make connections and apply their knowledge to similar situations? Do they use mathematical content from levels 1 and 2 to solve problems and investigate?

Name ______________________ Date ____________

How can you measure each worm?

How long do you think each worm is? Make an estimate, then find a way to measure each one.

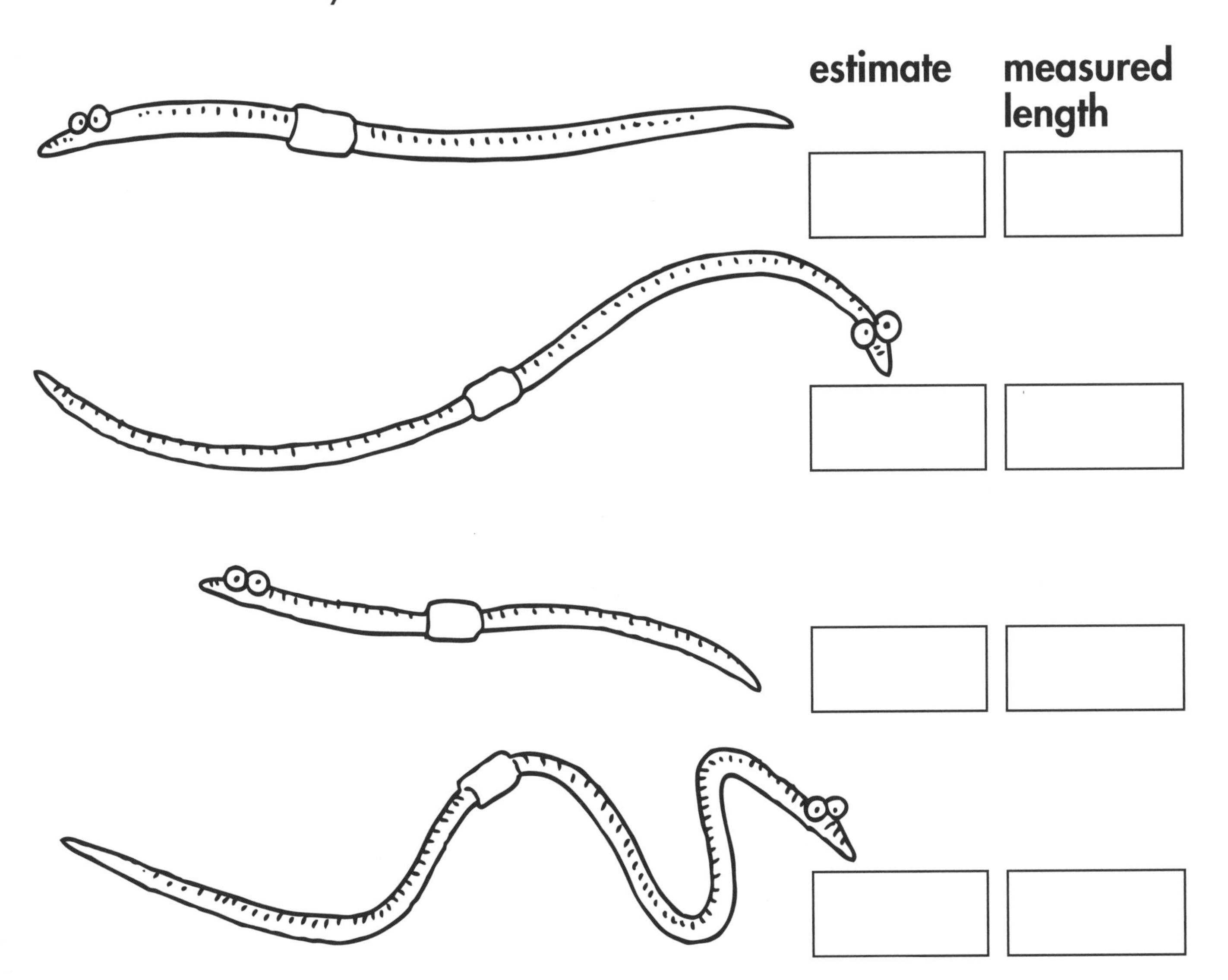

Teacher's notes

Suggested objective: ***Find a way to measure the worms.***

Problems: ***How long do you think each worm is? How can you measure each worm?***
Encourage the children to estimate appropriately then to think of ways to measure the length of each worm – for example, they could choose to use pieces of string or unit cubes.

Name ______________________ Date ______________

How can you measure each tail?

Sheet 91

How long do you think each tail is? Make an estimate, then find a way to measure each one.

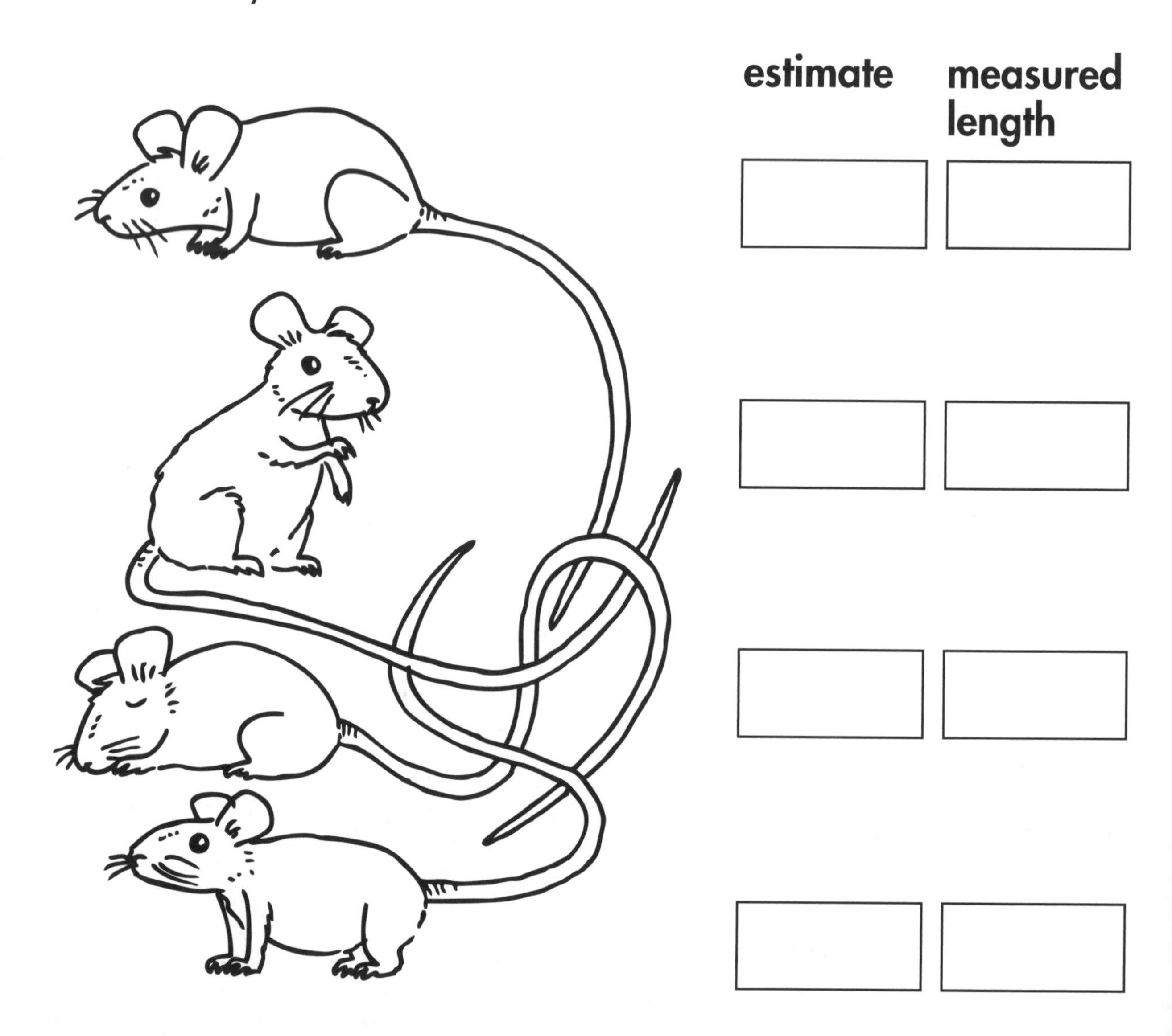

Teacher's notes

Suggested objective: ***Find a way to measure the tails.***

Problems: ***How long do you think each mouse's tail is? How can you measure each tail?***
Encourage the children to estimate appropriately then to think of ways to measure the length of each tail – for example, they could choose to use pieces of string or unit cubes.

Name ______________________ Date __________

How long is a piece of string?

How long do you think each piece of string is? Make an estimate, then find a way to measure each one.

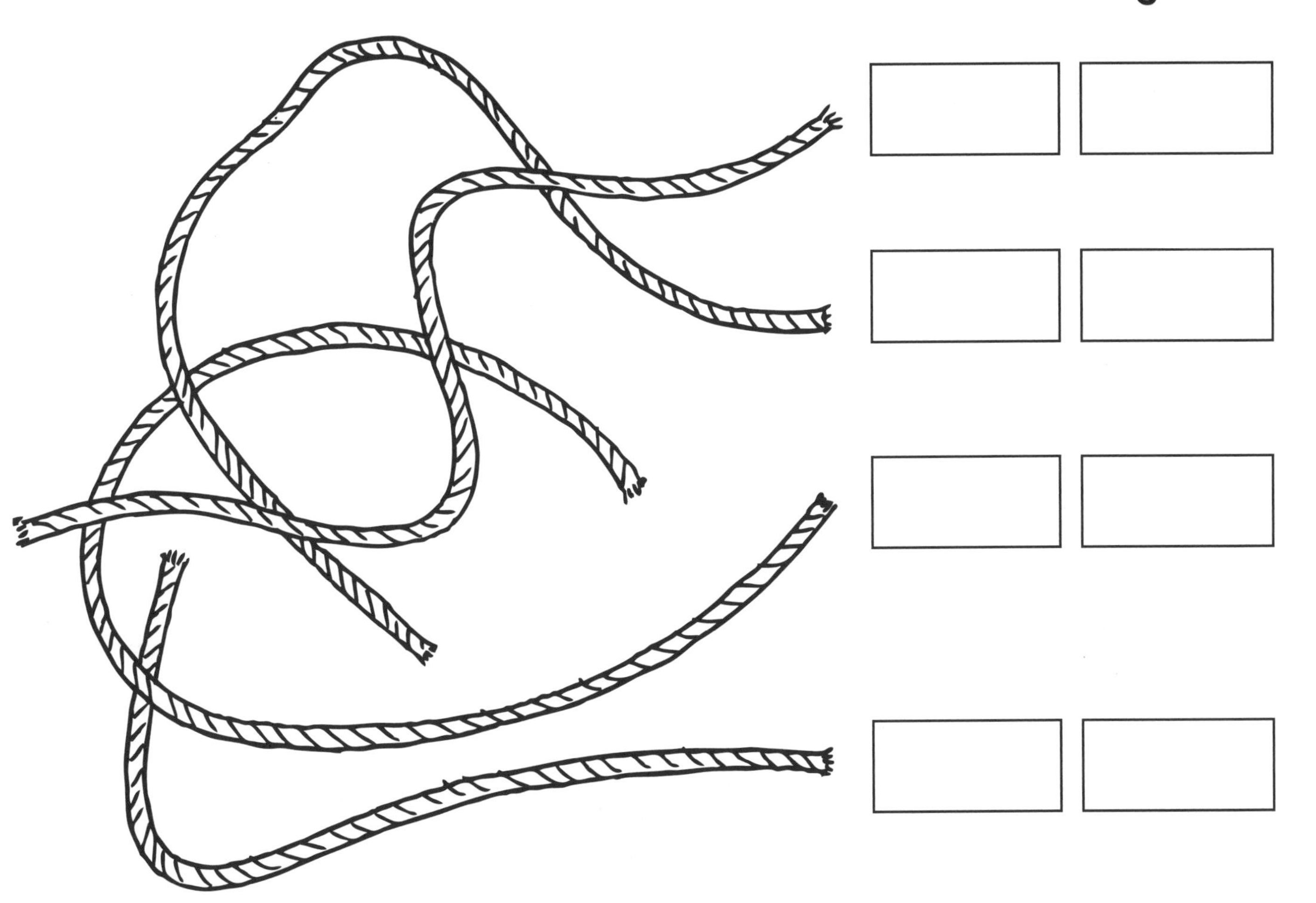

estimate	measured length

Teacher's notes

Suggested objective: ***Find a way to measure the string.***

Problems: ***How long do you think each piece of string is? How can you measure each piece?***
Encourage the children to estimate appropriately then to think of ways to measure the length of each piece of string – they could choose to use real pieces of string to lay next to the pictures or unit cubes.

Name ______________________ Date __________

How heavy are the teddies?

Sheet 93

How heavy is Ted? [ ]

How heavy is Tim? [ ]

How heavy is Tom? [ ]

Which teddy is heaviest? [ ]

Which teddy is lightest? [ ]

How much heavier than Ted is Tom? [ ]

How much heavier than Tim is Tom? [ ]

What is the total weight of the three teddies? [ ]

Teacher's notes

Suggested objective: ***Read weights on scales.***

Problems: Children answer the questions above. In observing them dealing with the questions you are able to assess several aspects of the Assessment Focuses for Using and Applying Mathematics and for Shape, Space and Measures: Do they find a starting point, identifying key facts/relevant information? Do they adopt a suggested model or systematic approach? Do they make connections and apply their knowledge to similar situations? Do they understand that numbers can be used to describe continuous measures? Are they beginning to use everyday non-standard and standard units to measure length and mass?

Name ______________________ Date ____________

How heavy are the cats?

Sheet 94

How heavy is Mog?

How heavy is Daz?

How heavy is Tig?

Which cat is heaviest?

Which cat is lightest?

How much heavier than Mog is Tig?

How much heavier than Mog is Daz?

What is the total weight of the three cats?

Teacher's notes

Suggested objective: ***Read weights on scales.***

Problems: Children answer the questions above. In observing them dealing with the questions you are able to assess several aspects of the Assessment Focuses for Using and Applying Mathematics and for Shape, Space and Measures: Do they find a starting point, identifying key facts/relevant information? Do they adopt a suggested model or systematic approach? Do they make connections and apply their knowledge to similar situations? Do they understand that numbers can be used to describe continuous measures? Are they beginning to use everyday non-standard and standard units to measure length and mass?

Name ______________________ Date ____________

How heavy are the dogs?

Sheet 95

How heavy is Rex? ☐

How heavy is Tip? ☐

How heavy is Pug? ☐

Which dog is heaviest? ☐

Which dog is lightest? ☐

How much heavier than Pug is Rex? ☐

How much heavier than Tip is Rex? ☐

What is the total weight of the three dogs? ☐

Teacher's notes

Suggested objective: ***Read weights on scales.***

Problems: Children answer the questions above. In observing them dealing with the questions you are able to assess several aspects of the Assessment Focuses for Using and Applying Mathematics and for Shape, Space and Measures: Do they find a starting point, identifying key facts/relevant information? Do they adopt a suggested model or systematic approach? Do they make connections and apply their knowledge to similar situations? Do they understand that numbers can be used to describe continuous measures? Are they beginning to use everyday non-standard and standard units to measure length and mass?

Name ______________________ Date ______________

Which is the most expensive item?

chocolate muffin £2.50

Teacher's notes

Suggested objective: ***Solve problems involving money.***

Problems: ***Which is the most expensive item?***
Which is the least expensive item? What is the total cost of the items? How much more is a coffee than a tea? Note that this activity provides the opportunity for pupils to 'solve problems involving addition, subtraction' … 'in contexts of numbers, measures or pounds and pence'.

Name ______________________ Date ____________

Sheet 97

Which is the least expensive item?

blueberry muffin £2.50

orange juice £2

bottle of water £1

chocolate crisp cake £1.50

flapjack £1.50

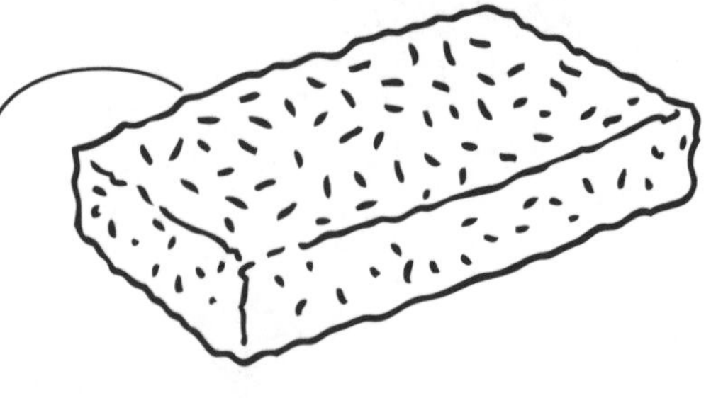

Teacher's notes

Suggested objective: ***Solve problems involving money.***

Problems: ***Which is the most expensive item? Which is the least expensive item?***
What is the total cost of the items? How much more is a blueberry muffin than a flapjack?

Name ____________________ Date ____________

What is the total cost of the items?

sandwiches £2.80

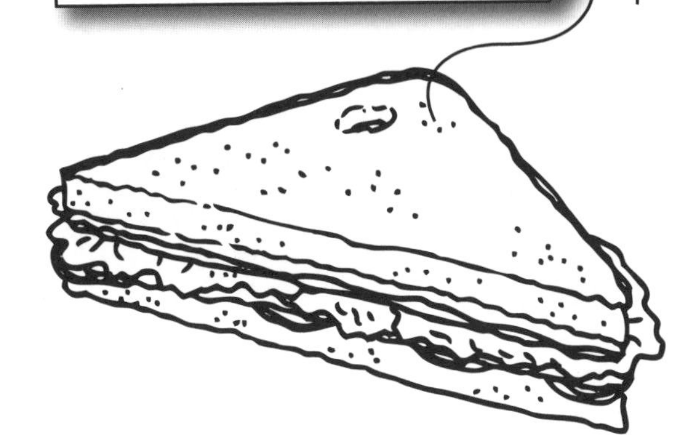

hot chocolate £2.75

panini £3.20

milk £1.25

Teacher's notes

Suggested objective: ***Solve problems involving money.***

Problems: ***Which is the most expensive item? Which is the least expensive item?*** What is the total cost of the items? How much more is a panini than a sandwich?

Name ______________________ Date ____________

What are you going to buy at the coffee shop?

coffee £2

tea £1.50

flapjack £1.50

chocolate crisp cake £1.50

chocolate muffin £2.50

blueberry muffin £2.50

biscuit £1

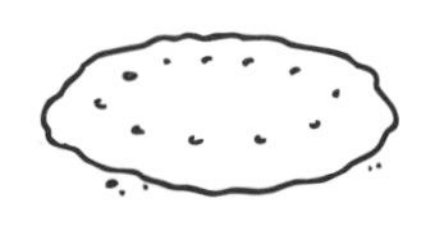

smoothie £2

bottle of water £1

orange juice £2

Teacher's notes

This actvity sheet to be used in conjunction with Sheets 100 and 101.
Suggested objective: ***Solve problems involving money.***

Problems: ***You and your mum are at the coffee shop. You can spend up to £10 on both of you. Which items will you buy? How much will they cost altogether? What change will you get from £10?***
Ask the children to cut out the items to record their purchases on Sheet 101.

Name ______________________ Date ______________

Sheet 100

What are you going to buy at the coffee shop?

coffee £2

tea £1.50

panini £3.20

flap-jack £1.50

chocolate crisp cake £1.50

chocolate muffin £2.50

blueberry muffin £2.50

sandwiches £2.80

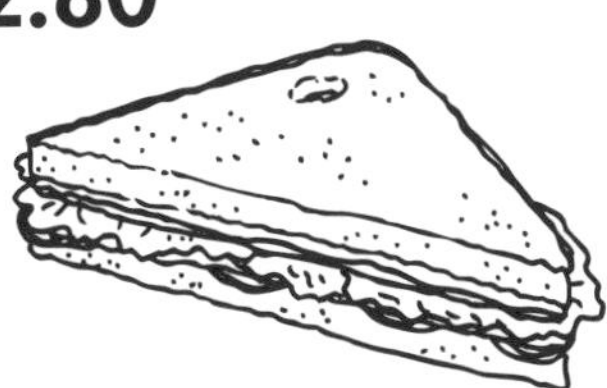

hot chocolate £2.75

biscuit £1

orange juice £2

smoothie £2

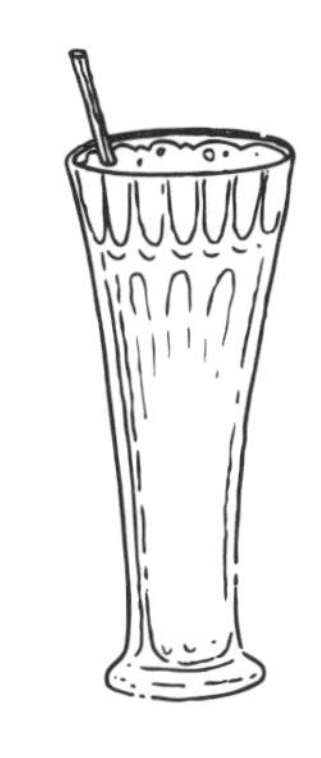

bottle of water £1

milk £1.25

Teacher's notes

This activity sheet to be used in conjunction with Sheet 101.
Suggested objective: ***Solve problems involving money.***

Problems: ***You and your mum are at the coffee shop. You can spend up to £10 on both of you. Which items will you buy? How much will they cost altogether? What change will you get from £10?***
Ask the children to cut out the items to record their purchases on Sheet 101.

Name ______________________ Date ____________

Sheet 101

How much are you spending?

You and your mum are at the coffee shop with up to £10 to spend. Which items will you buy?

item	cost

How much do your items cost altogether? [ ]

What change will you get from £10? [ ]

Teacher's notes

Suggested objective: ***Solve problems involving money.***

Problems: Support the children in answering the problems on the sheet. This sheet should be completed after the children have had the opportunity to discuss the coffee shop items shown on the previous sheets. They need to make decisions about what to buy, ensuring that the total cost comes to £10 or less. They can write the names of the items or they can stick the appropriate pictures in the left-hand column of the table, then find the total and the change, if any.

Extension Problem: Increase the number of customers buying items at the coffee shop.

Name ______________________________ Date ____________

How much have I spent?

Sheet 102

10p

20p

50p

£1

I spend 10p and 20p. How much have I spent altogether? ☐

I spend 10p and 40p. How much have I spent altogether? ☐

I spend 50p and 20p. How much have I spent altogether? ☐

I spend 20p and 20p. How much have I spent altogether? ☐

I spend 40p and 20p. How much have I spent altogether? ☐

I spend 30p and 20p. How much have I spent altogether? ☐

I spend 60p and 30p. How much have I spent altogether? ☐

I spend 40p and 30p. How much have I spent altogether? ☐

I spend 60p and 40p. How much have I spent altogether? ☐

Teacher's notes

Suggested objective: ***Solve problems involving money.***

Problems: Support the children in answering the problems above.
Extension problem: Ask the children what the change would be from £1 for each of the amounts spent. This activity provides the opportunity for pupils to 'solve problems involving addition, subtraction' … 'in contexts of numbers, measures or pounds and pence' while working with multiples of 10 with totals up to 100.

Name ______________________ Date ____________

How much have I spent?

Sheet 103

I spend 15p and 20p. How much have I spent altogether? ☐

I spend 23p and 10p. How much have I spent altogether? ☐

I spend 16p and 10p. How much have I spent altogether? ☐

I spend 28p and 20p. How much have I spent altogether? ☐

I spend 35p and 30p. How much have I spent altogether? ☐

I spend 42p and 20p. How much have I spent altogether? ☐

I spend 57p and 30p. How much have I spent altogether? ☐

I spend 63p and 30p. How much have I spent altogether? ☐

I spend 31p and 50p. How much have I spent altogether? ☐

Teacher's notes

Suggested objective: ***Solve problems involving money.***

Problems: Support the children in answering the problems above. This activity provides the opportunity for pupils to 'solve problems involving addition, subtraction' … 'in contexts of numbers, measures or pounds and pence' while adding mentally a multiple of 10 to any two-digit number.
Extension problem: Ask what the change would be from £1 for each of the amounts spent.

Name ______________________ Date ____________

How much have I spent?

Sheet 104

1p 2p 5p 10p 20p 50p £1

I spend 25p and 4p. How much have I spent altogether? ☐

I spend 26p and 5p. How much have I spent altogether? ☐

I spend 34p and 6p. How much have I spent altogether? ☐

I spend 43p and 8p. How much have I spent altogether? ☐

I spend 56p and 7p. How much have I spent altogether? ☐

I spend 68p and 5p. How much have I spent altogether? ☐

I spend 75p and 9p. How much have I spent altogether? ☐

I spend 93p and 7p. How much have I spent altogether? ☐

I spend 84p and 8p. How much have I spent altogether? ☐

Teacher's notes

Suggested objective: ***Solve problems involving money.***

Problems: Support the children in answering the problems above. This activity provides the opportunity for pupils to 'solve problems involving addition, subtraction' … 'in contexts of numbers, measures or pounds and pence' while adding mentally a one-digit number to any two-digit number.
Extension problem: Ask what the change would be from £1 for each of the amounts spent.

Name ______________________ Date __________

What is my change from £1?

Sheet 105

10p

20p

50p

£1

What is my change from £1 when I spend 50p? ☐

What is my change from £1 when I spend 70p? ☐

What is my change from £1 when I spend 10p? ☐

What is my change from £1 when I spend 80p? ☐

What is my change from £1 when I spend 40p? ☐

What is my change from £1 when I spend 60p? ☐

What is my change from £1 when I spend 90p? ☐

What is my change from £1 when I spend 30p? ☐

What is my change from £1 when I spend 20p? ☐

Teacher's notes

Suggested objective: ***Solve problems involving money.***

Problems: Support the children in answering the problems above. This activity provides the opportunity for pupils to 'solve problems involving addition, subtraction' … 'in contexts of numbers, measures or pounds and pence' while working with multiples of 10 with a total of 100.

Name ______________________ Date ____________

What is my change?

Sheet 106

10p

20p

50p

£1

What is my change from 50p when I spend 30p? ☐

What is my change from 90p when I spend 20p? ☐

What is my change from 50p when I spend 40p? ☐

What is my change from 70p when I spend 30p? ☐

What is my change from 90p when I spend 50p? ☐

What is my change from 60p when I spend 20p? ☐

What is my change from 40p when I spend 30p? ☐

What is my change from 60p when I spend 30p? ☐

What is my change from 80p when I spend 50p? ☐

Teacher's notes

Suggested objective: ***Solve problems involving money.***

Problems: Support the children in answering the problems above. This activity provides the opportunity for pupils to 'solve problems involving addition, subtraction' … 'in contexts of numbers, measures or pounds and pence' while working with multiples of 10 with totals up to 100.

Name ____________________ Date ____________

What is my change?

Sheet 107

1p

2p

5p

10p

20p

50p

£1

What is my change from 20p when I spend 6p? ☐

What is my change from 30p when I spend 8p? ☐

What is my change from 50p when I spend 4p? ☐

What is my change from 70p when I spend 8p? ☐

What is my change from 90p when I spend 2p? ☐

What is my change from 20p when I spend 9p? ☐

What is my change from 40p when I spend 1p? ☐

What is my change from 60p when I spend 3p? ☐

What is my change from 80p when I spend 5p? ☐

Teacher's notes

Suggested objective: ***Solve problems involving money.***

Problems: Support the children in answering the problems above. This activity provides the opportunity for pupils to 'solve problems involving addition, subtraction' … 'in contexts of numbers, measures or pounds and pence' while subtracting mentally a one-digit number from any two-digit number.

Name ______________________ Date ____________

What time is it?

Word bank

o'clock half past
quarter past quarter to
one two three four five
six seven eight nine
ten eleven twelve

What time does the clock show?

What time will it be an hour and a half later?

What time will it be two and a quarter hours later?

What time will it be four and a half hours later?

What time will it be one and three-quarter hours later?

Teacher's notes

Suggested objective: ***Solve problems about time.***

Problems: Children answer the questions above. They will need to interpret the questions, understanding the vocabulary of time. You could provide a geared clock for them to use. Ensure that the children understand that each question refers to the original time shown on the clock.

Name ______________________ Date ____________

What time will it be?

Sheet 109

Word bank

o'clock half past
quarter past quarter to
one two three four five
six seven eight nine
ten eleven twelve

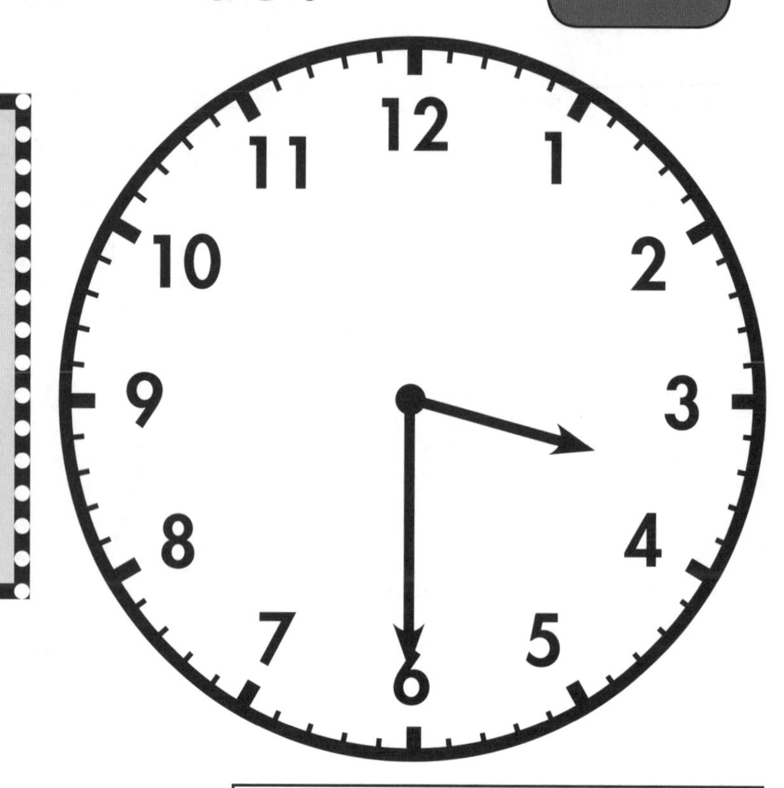

What time does the clock show?

What time will it be an hour and a half later?

What time will it be a quarter of an hour later?

What time will it be an hour and a quarter later?

What time will it be two hours and a quarter later?

Teacher's notes

Suggested objective: ***Solve problems about time: half past.***

Problems: Children answer the questions above. They will need to interpret the questions, understanding the vocabulary of time. You could provide a geared clock for them to use. Ensure that the children understand that each question refers to the original time shown on the clock.

Name ______________________ Date ____________

What time will it be?

Sheet 110

Word bank

o'clock half past
quarter past quarter to
one two three four five
six seven eight nine
ten eleven twelve

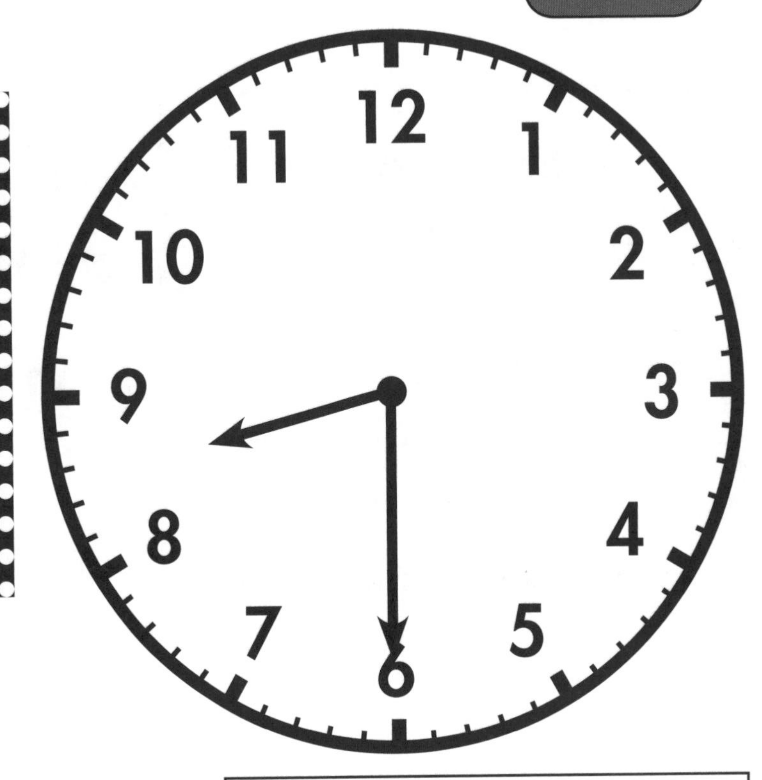

What time does the clock show? [ ]

What time will it be quarter of an hour later? [ ]

What time will it be half an hour later? [ ]

What time will it be three quarters of an hour later? [ ]

What time will it be an hour and a quarter later? [ ]

Teacher's notes

Suggested objective: ***Solve problems about time: half past.***

Problems: Children answer the questions above. They will need to interpret the questions, understanding the vocabulary of time. You could provide a geared clock for them to use. Ensure that the children understand that each question refers to the original time shown on the clock.

Name ______________________ Date ____________

What time was it?

Sheet 111

Word bank

o'clock half past
quarter past quarter to
one two three four five
six seven eight nine
ten eleven twelve

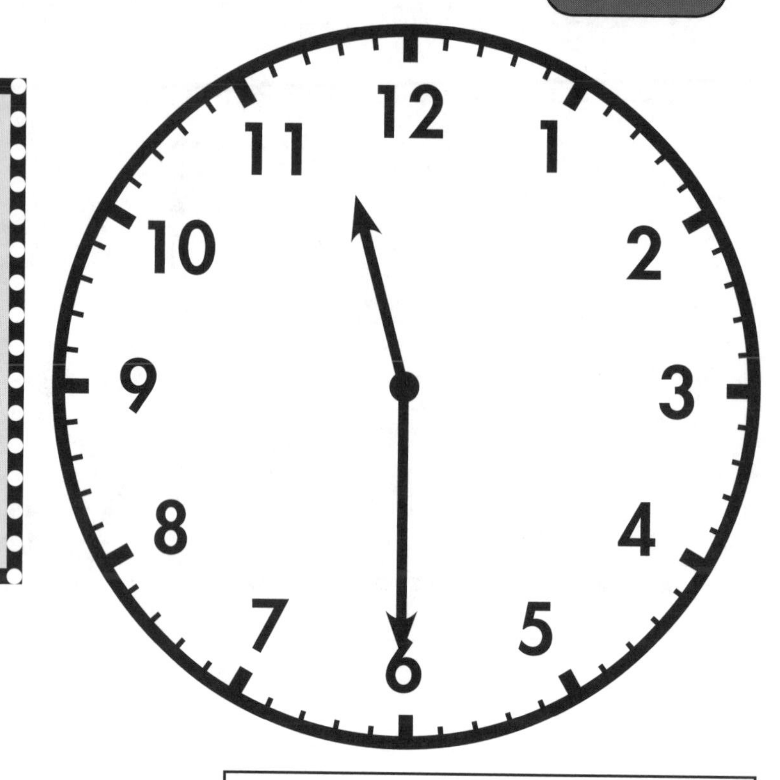

What time does the clock show? [ ]

What time was it a quarter of an hour before this time? [ ]

What time was it half an hour before this time? [ ]

What time was it an hour before this time? [ ]

What time was it an hour and a half before this time? [ ]

Teacher's notes

Suggested objective: ***Solve problems about time: half past.***

Problems: Children answer the questions above. They will need to interpret the questions, understanding the vocabulary of time. You could provide a geared clock for them to use. Ensure that the children understand that each question refers to the original time shown on the clock.

Name ______________________ Date ____________

What time will it be?

Sheet 112

Word bank

o'clock half past
quarter past quarter to
one two three four five
six seven eight nine
ten eleven twelve

What time does the clock show? [ ]

What time will it be a quarter of an hour later? [ ]

What time will it be half an hour later? [ ]

What time will it be three quarters of an hour later? [ ]

What time will it be an hour later? [ ]

Teacher's notes

Suggested objective: ***Solve problems about time: quarter past.***

Problems: Children answer the questions above. They will need to interpret the questions, understanding the vocabulary of time. You could provide a geared clock for them to use. Ensure that the children understand that each question refers to the original time shown on the clock.

Name ____________________ Date __________

What time will it be?

Sheet 113

Word bank

o'clock half past
quarter past quarter to
one two three four five
six seven eight nine
ten eleven twelve

What time does the clock show? ☐

What time will it be a quarter of an hour later? ☐

What time will it be half an hour later? ☐

What time will it be three quarters of an hour later? ☐

What time will it be an hour later? ☐

Teacher's notes

Suggested objective: ***Solve problems about time: quarter past.***

Problems: Children answer the questions above. They will need to interpret the questions, understanding the vocabulary of time. You could provide a geared clock for them to use so that they can 'answer a question by selecting and using suitable equipment'. Ensure that the children understand that each question refers to the original time shown on the clock.

Name ______________________ Date ____________

What time will it be?

Sheet 114

Word bank

o'clock half past
quarter past quarter to
one two three four five
six seven eight nine
ten eleven twelve

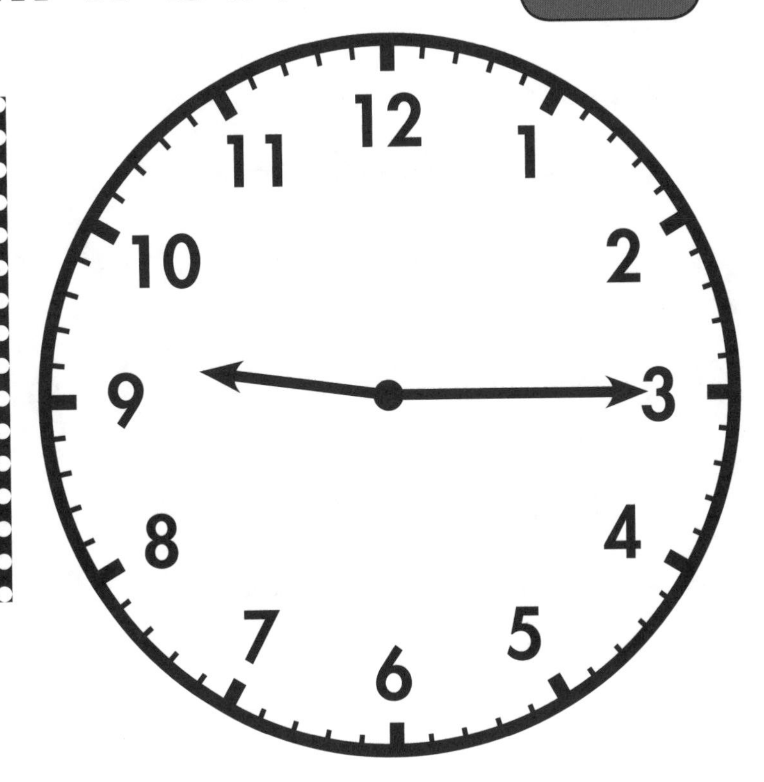

What time does the clock show?

What time will it be a quarter of an hour later?

What time will it be half an hour later?

What time will it be three quarters of an hour later?

What time will it be an hour later?

Teacher's notes

Suggested objective: ***Solve problems about time: quarter past.***

Problems: Children answer the questions above. They will need to interpret the questions, understanding the vocabulary of time. You could provide a geared clock for them to use so that they can 'answer a question by selecting and using suitable equipment'. Ensure that the children understand that each question refers to the original time shown on the clock.

Name ______________________ Date ____________

What time will it be?

Sheet 115

Word bank

o'clock half past
quarter past quarter to
one two three four five
six seven eight nine
ten eleven twelve

What time does the clock show?

What time will it be a quarter of an hour later?

What time will it be an hour later?

What time will it be an hour and a quarter later?

What time will it be two hours later?

Teacher's notes

Suggested objective: ***Solve problems about time: quarter past.***

Problems: Children answer the questions above. They will need to interpret the questions, understanding the vocabulary of time. You could provide a geared clock for them to use so that they can 'answer a question by selecting and using suitable equipment'. Ensure that the children understand that each question refers to the original time shown on the clock.

Name ______________________ Date __________

What time will it be?

Word bank

o'clock half past
quarter past quarter to
one two three four five
six seven eight nine
ten eleven twelve

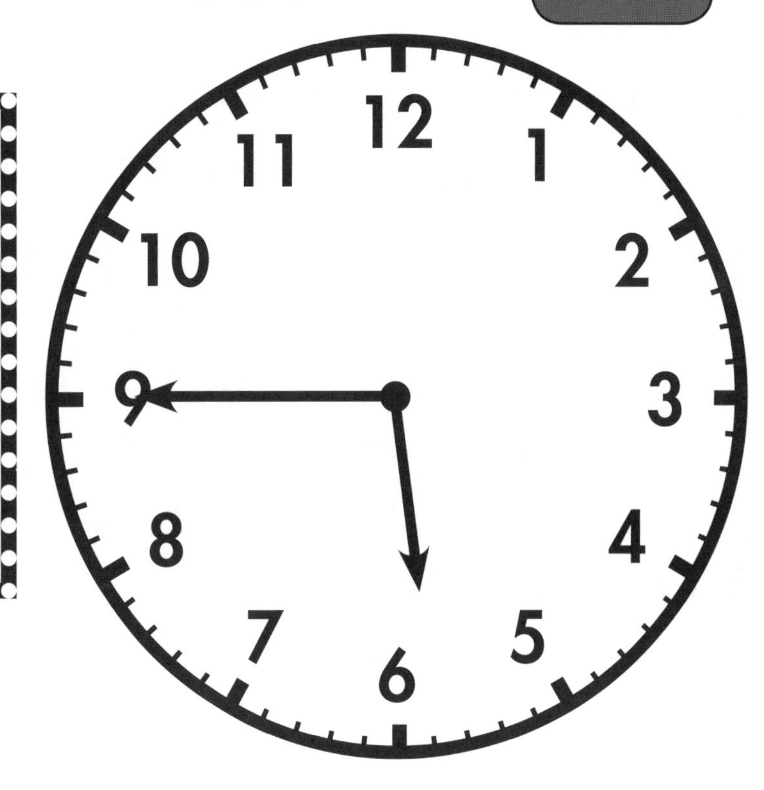

What time does the clock show? [ ]

What time will it be a quarter of an hour later? [ ]

What time will it be half an hour later? [ ]

What time will it be three quarters of an hour later? [ ]

What time will it be an hour later? [ ]

Teacher's notes

Suggested objective: ***Solve problems about time: quarter to.***

Problems: Children answer the questions above. They will need to interpret the questions, understanding the vocabulary of time. You could provide a geared clock for them to use so that they can 'answer a question by selecting and using suitable equipment'. Ensure that the children understand that each question refers to the original time shown on the clock.

Name ______________________ Date ____________

What time will it be?

Sheet 117

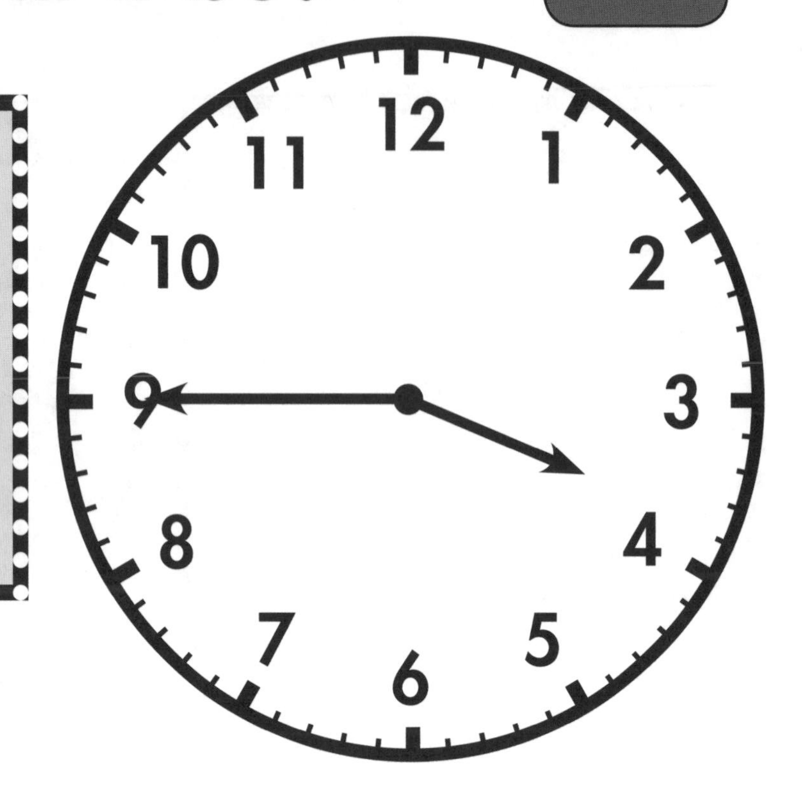

Word bank

o'clock half past
quarter past quarter to
one two three four five
six seven eight nine
ten eleven twelve

What time does the clock show? [ ]

What time will it be a quarter of an hour later? [ ]

What time will it be half an hour later? [ ]

What time will it be three quarters of an hour later? [ ]

What time will it be an hour later? [ ]

Teacher's notes

Suggested objective: ***Solve problems about time: quarter to.***

Problems: Children answer the questions above. They will need to interpret the questions, understanding the vocabulary of time. You could provide a geared clock for them to use so that they can 'answer a question by selecting and using suitable equipment'. Ensure that the children understand that each question refers to the original time shown on the clock.

Name ______________________ Date __________

What time will it be?

Word bank

o'clock half past
quarter past quarter to
one two three four five
six seven eight nine
ten eleven twelve

What time does the clock show?

What time will it be a quarter of an hour later?

What time will it be an hour and a quarter later?

What time will it be half an hour later?

What time will it be two and a half hours later?

Teacher's notes

Suggested objective: ***Solve problems about time: quarter to.***

Problems: Children answer the questions above. They will need to interpret the questions, understanding the vocabulary of time. You could provide a geared clock for them to use so that they can 'answer a question by selecting and using suitable equipment'. Ensure that the children understand that each question refers to the original time shown on the clock.

Name ______________________ Date __________

Sheet 119

What numbers fit in the gaps?

Look carefully at the puzzle. It has a target number of 12.
You need to write some numbers to make a subtraction sentence and an addition sentence both with the answer 12.
Here are the numbers you must use: 9, 2, 14 and 3.

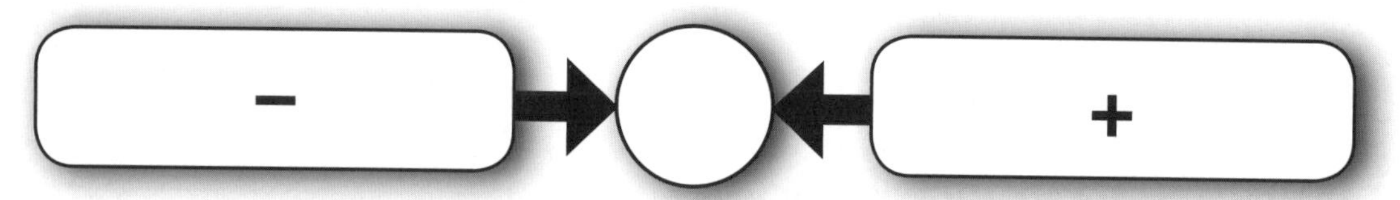

Look carefully at the puzzle. This time you have to find the number in the middle as well.
Here are the numbers you must use: 3, 4, 11, 15 and 18.

Look carefully at the puzzle.
Here are the numbers you must use: 6, 8, 9, 14 and 23.

Teacher's notes

Suggested objective: ***Find patterns and relationships involving numbers.***

Problem: ***Can you find the numbers to fill the gaps?***
Do the children use the knowledge that subtraction is the inverse of addition? Do the children use mental recall of addition and subtraction facts? Do they adopt a systematic approach? Do they make connections and apply their knowledge to similar situations? Do they present solutions to puzzles and problems in an organized way?